COPPER PIPE-LINE SERVICES
IN BUILDING

*End view of the ancient Egyptian
copper water pipe shown overleaf.*

FRONTISPIECE   *A piece of ancient Egyptian copper water pipe, which is dated c. 2750 B.C. The tube has an internal diameter of about 3 in. and formed part of a pipe-line nearly 300 yards in length, made up of separate sections each about 2 ft. 6 in. long. The tube was folded up from thin hand-hammered copper sheet and embedded in gypsum in stone hewn out to U shape. (For end view of tube, see previous page.)*

COPPER PIPE-LINE SERVICES IN BUILDING

A PRACTICAL HANDBOOK

—

Published by the

COPPER DEVELOPMENT ASSOCIATION

55, SOUTH AUDLEY STREET · LONDON, W.1.

Telephone No.: Grosvenor 8811

C.D.A. Publication No. 25
First issued, 1938; 18th revised impression,
1957

CONTENTS

PLATES

TABLES

FOREWORD AND ACKNOWLEDGMENTS

The purpose of this book is to collect within one volume much of the theoretical and practical information on copper pipe-line services in building which exists in published or unpublished form but which is too scattered for easy reference. It is hoped that designers and craftsmen will find the book a useful guide to the principal uses of copper pipes for hot and cold water services, heating, sanitation, gas services and electrical conduit, and to the techniques of jointing, bending and fitting, which are common to these uses. Unfortunately space does not permit the book to cover the other manifold and increasing uses of copper tubes in buildings, such as for air conditioning installations, vacuum cleaning suction plants, furnace oil feed pipe-lines, etc., for which copper is eminently suitable. A large part of the book is based upon long-established plumbing practice and accepted technique in the use of copper pipes, but it is hoped, nevertheless, that much of the information will be new to readers.

The Association gladly acknowledges the help it received from Mr. A. C. Martin, R.P., M.R.San.I., Mr. W. H. Fairclough, F.R.San.I., Mr. W. H. M. Smeaton, F.R.San.I., and Mr. A. Longworth, F.R.San.I., A.M.I.S.E., by the valuable assistance they rendered in the preparation of the first edition of this book.

Thanks are also due to the following for permission to publish in this edition photographs and tables, etc.: British Standards Institution, London, E.M.P. Engineering Co. Ltd., London, I.C.I. Ltd. Metals Division, Birmingham, W. G. Jenkinson Ltd., Sheffield, The Mint (Birmingham) Ltd., Northern Polytechnic, London, North Thames Gas Board, London, W. H. A. Robertson & Co. Ltd., Bedford, Rosser & Russell Ltd., London, W. H. Smith & Co., Leicester, and Yorkshire Copper Works Ltd., Leeds.

E. CARR,
November, 1957.

INTRODUCTION

The primary purpose of this handbook is to help the designer and the craftsman to a fuller understanding of the uses of copper and copper alloy pipes for the various kinds of installation work met with in buildings whether they be large or small. At the same time, it is hoped that the information contained in this volume will not be without interest to those whose work is connected with the teaching of students in the building industry.

To ensure that the fullest advantage is taken of the outstanding properties of copper tubes, the plumber and the designer should be fully acquainted with the physical properties of the metal and the characteristics which make it the ideal material for pipe lines of all kinds.

It is a significant fact that even fifty years ago many public buildings and institutions, having need of a permanent trouble-free installation, were equipped with copper tubes as a matter of course. In those days there was not available the degree of knowledge that we now possess regarding jointing methods, therefore the tubes used had a comparatively thick wall that would allow of a screw thread being cut into it. Under such conditions the cost of a copper installation was always comparatively high and yet despite this architects insisted on copper, knowing the advantages to be gained by its use.

With the advent of thin-walled or light gauge copper tubes, and the development of satisfactory methods of jointing them, the cost was brought down to a level highly competitive with that of other materials and a new era was opened up to the plumber and the heating engineer. Architects were quick to take advantage of the many good qualities that copper offered compared with other, and at that time more traditional, materials, with the result that the use of light gauge copper tubes rapidly became standard practice for domestic hot and cold water installations in all classes of building work, from small houses to blocks of luxury flats, hotels and hospitals, etc. Following on the use of light gauge copper tubes for these services, it soon became apparent that the many advantages to be gained were just as applicable to heating as to plumbing installations and so in this field also the use of copper tubes increased enormously. The next stage came when copper tubes were first considered for sanitary services. Here, the corrosion-resisting properties of the metal, together with the smooth internal surfaces of the tube, offered the sanitary engineer a material beyond reproach. With the advent of the so-called "one-pipe system" of soil and waste disposal, copper tubes were invariably specified.

For many years the gas industry had used heavy gauge brass tubes with screwed joints for short connections to gas fires and similar appliances, but it was not until about 1936 that the industry considered copper tubes for general carcassing work, although a few

Introduction of Light Gauge Copper tubing

9

of the more enlightened gas engineers had carried out trial installations with every satisfaction. The reasons for this apparent reluctance to use copper were economic, and with the lower prices that soon prevailed many of the larger gas undertakings changed over to copper entirely, thereby achieving a better job and, in addition, a saving in initial and maintenance costs.

Copper tube in long lengths

Another important development came with the introduction of long-length copper tubes in dead soft temper. These tubes, supplied in coils of varying lengths up to 60 ft., could be manipulated without the use of bending machines and springs and were ideal for panel heating, underground services, and for domestic hot and cold water services. They reduced the number of joints required and could be threaded into confined spaces easily. After a temporary setback during the war years the demand for soft copper tubes in coil has been renewed on an ever-increasing scale for water, heating and gas installations. This demand has been greatest for underground gas and water services from the street main to the consumer's premises, whilst similar pipe-lines for steam and hot water branches have been employed in connection with district heating schemes. For underground services, half-hard tubes in straight lengths are also used, especially for gas.

Use for Underground Services

All this did not come about haphazard, but was the result of many years of testing in both laboratory and field trials, which proved beyond doubt that the resistance of copper to soil corrosion was in general greater than that of any other material used for these services. Certain gas and water authorities in this country had experimented with copper for underground use, and being more than satisfied with the results, allowed its unrestricted use in their own areas. In some cases, the copper has been giving trouble-free service for as long as thirty years and samples removed for examination have been found to be in perfect condition. Of course, much other evidence of the excellent lasting qualities of copper and its alloys, and their resistance to the action of the elements and of soils, is to be found in museums all the world over. It is, however, sufficient to draw attention to the frontispiece, which is particularly applicable to the subject of this book.

Resistance to Corrosion

Copper's resistance to corrosion is due to the formation, by natural processes, of a protective film which in nearly all cases renders the metal safe from attack by the atmosphere and from any water, gas or soil with which it may be in contact. The film is primarily an oxidised layer which forms a protective skin on both the inside and the outside of copper pipes and ensures, not only a very long life for the pipe, but also that it will not contaminate drinking water or require any additional treatment for protection when installed in contact with the usual building materials or normal types of soil.

Copper pipes cannot rust and so do not require painting, which saves cost and, in the case of hot water pipes, avoids the unpleasant smell of warm paint. In certain cases where the pipes are run on the surface, the attractive appearance of the metal can be exploited to fit in with the surrounding decorative features. To-day, however, the trend in modern building is to conceal the plumbing work as much as possible, with the result that many of the pipes are installed in chases or are buried in the walls and floors.

Concrete, lime and lime plasters and cement mortar have no harmful effect on copper, but certain acid soils and materials are known to be corrosive to all metals, and the methods to be adopted to insulate copper pipes under such conditions are discussed fully in the chapters on Underground Services and Gas Fitting (see pages 74 and 116).

In addition to their corrosion-resisting properties, copper pipes possess a combination of physical characteristics not found in other pipe materials. The ductility of the metal allows them to be manipulated with ease, whilst the strength of even light gauge tubes ensures that they will withstand pressures far higher than those to be found in normal water supply services, e.g., the pressure required to burst a $\frac{1}{2}$ in. × 19 S.W.G. half-hard copper tube is 5,900 lb. per square inch. They will also withstand considerable external pressures and adjust themselves to irregularities and settlements in soils or buildings without risk of fractures occurring.

Other Physical Advantages of Copper

In many cases, waste one-pipe soil pipes are subjected to expansion and contraction due to changes in temperature, and restraint of the consequent movement at various points in the installation may set up stresses in the pipes. Copper combines sufficient strength and elasticity to prevent any permanent deformation such as that which occurs in soft metal pipes under similar conditions. In the case of heating installations carried out in light gauge copper pipes, there is economy in the amount of metal used with consequent saving in cost, weight and space; a smaller mass of metal to be heated, and less radiation surface for heat loss, thereby effecting a saving in fuel. The ease with which the tubes can be handled, manipulated and jointed means lower labour costs and reduction in the number of fittings required as compared with a similar installation in iron.

Strength and Elasticity of Copper

The very smooth surfaces of a solid drawn copper tube are important, particularly in water pipes, because of the low frictional resistance which they offer to the flow of the water, and in soil and waste services because they reduce the risk of blockages to a minimum. In hard water districts, the calcium carbonate deposits do not adhere so quickly or so firmly to the smooth interior surfaces of copper pipes and therefore these do not become blocked so readily, while the removal of the scale, when necessary, is much easier than from iron pipes.

Smooth bore of Copper tubes

From a decorative point of view, the smooth non-rusting exterior surfaces have much to commend them; they can be polished easily and readily take a plated finish. The small overall diameter of the pipes and joints presents a neat and tidy appearance.

A further interesting point arising from the smooth bore of a copper tube is that it affords, in conjunction with the strength and ductility of copper, a measure of protection against frost bursting. It is not claimed that copper pipes will not burst under extreme conditions of cold, and no good plumber would expose any type of installation to such conditions; a further reference to this point will be found on page 84.

The advantages referred to in the previous pages are not new discoveries, for, as stated at the outset, copper pipes have long been accepted as giving the very best job. Their general acceptance was, however, delayed largely because of exaggerated ideas of the first cost of a copper installation, and it is still often not realised that such an installation is very much cheaper than in lead and is competitive with galvanised iron. Further, considerable savings in initial cost can be achieved where prefabrication of quantity repetition units is carried out. Copper is by far the most suitable material for this type of work, for copper tubes, while being easy to fabricate and joint, are light and easy to handle, yet are strong enough to resist damage in transport and combine considerable rigidity with a degree of flexibility sufficient to take up the variations in dimensions ordinarily met with when fixing on site. Soil and waste pipe installations in copper also lend themselves to this form of construction and the enormous reduction in site labour costs more than offsets the cost of jigs and tools.

To-day the plumbing trade realises that copper has become a part of their craft and every technical college teaching plumbing includes copper work in its curriculum.

Function of the C.D.A.

In this work the Copper Development Association has taken, and continues to take, a considerable part. The Association is a non-trading organisation maintained by the British copper industry, and one of its primary objects is to provide assistance and information on the subject of copper for those who will be called upon to carry out work in the metal. In relation to building, the services of the Association are available to all from architect to plumber, as well as to students.

Facilities offered by the C.D.A.

The Association provides technical information of both a practical and theoretical nature and has at its disposal a very considerable volume of data for this purpose. When necessary, however, investigations are carried out to help in the elucidation of new problems and this and the other services which the Association offers, is available to all, whether public bodies or private individuals, without charge or obligation.

The necessity sometimes arises for placing inquirers in touch with sources of supply of approved materials, and this the C.D.A. undertakes to do while making every endeavour to avoid recommending any one manufacturer at the expense of others equally fitted to supply the same goods.

A similar service is that of establishing contact between those who wish to use copper and craftsmen capable of carrying out such work in an approved manner. The C.D.A., with the co-operation of the official plumbing organisations, has inaugurated a Register for this purpose. It is of mutual benefit for firms and individuals who are capable of undertaking various branches of copper work to communicate with the Association indicating what types of work they are prepared to undertake.

Architects, engineers, plumbers and others sometimes wish to know whether a given water is suitable for conveyance in copper pipes. In this respect the C.D.A. offers, when necessary, a free analytical service which operates in the following manner. Samples of the water taken under prescribed conditions in containers supplied for the purpose are sent by the inquirer to the analysts, an independent and authoritative body, who carry out a detailed analysis and certain tests, the results of which, with a report, are submitted to the C.D.A. The Association, in turn, places before the inquirer all the information obtained, together with any relevant comments, such as suggestions for the treatment of the water should it prove corrosive to metals. The C.D.A. already possesses a large number of analyses of the waters supplied by various authorities throughout the country, so that a fresh analysis is not necessary in every case.

It is realised that much still remains to be done if a full and widespread knowledge of copper work is to be achieved. To this end, the Association will upon request provide free to technical schools and other organisations lectures on copper, illustrated by lantern slides and with practical demonstrations when necessary. Aids to teaching such as wall charts, models, etc., are also provided in certain cases upon request.

Much published information on copper exists, but in a scattered form. The Association has made it part of its activities to collect, and where necessary to republish, such information, and constantly to break new ground in specialised subjects where technical books are felt to be desirable and necessary. Publications issued by the C.D.A. are available to all those professionally or technically interested, and a list is appended at the end of this book.

C.D.A. Technical Publications

CHAPTER I

THE MANUFACTURE OF COPPER TUBES

Whilst this book is a practical textbook on the use of copper tubes in plumbing, it may not be out of place briefly to describe how such tubes are manufactured.

Quality of B.S. Tubes

Copper tubes supplied in accordance with British Standards must be made of high quality copper from which oxygen has been removed by the addition of a small quantity of phosphorus and to which may have been added, if desired, a small quantity of arsenic. Refined copper is therefore first melted and after the addition of the phosphorus, with or without arsenic, the molten metal is cast into billets of circular cross section, usually about two to six inches in diameter, and about four feet long. The metal is then known as "deoxidised" copper and is described as "arsenical" or "non-arsenical" according to whether it contains arsenic or not.

Stages of Manufacture

The first stage in the production of a tube is to pierce the solid billet longitudinally and make it into a rough tube shell. This is done either by a rotary piercing process or by extrusion. In the former process, the heated billet, at a temperature of about 850° to 900° C. is forced between specially shaped conical rollers which cause it, rather surprisingly, to open up inside to form a rough tube which is then pushed forward over a supporting mandrel (*See* Plate I, p. 20).

With the extrusion process a shorter billet is used and this at a suitably high temperature is placed in a container and the metal forced by a hydraulically operated ram through an annular space formed between the walls of a circular die and a centrally placed mandrel in the end of the container.

The tube shell produced by either of these methods is next subjected to a series of cold drawing operations by which it is elongated and thinned. This is achieved by drawing the tube through a series of progressively smaller steel dies, the tube being supported on the inside either by a long steel mandrel threaded through it or by a plug held in position at the point at which the tube passes through the die. The tube is squeezed between the mandrel or plug and the die and so its wall thickness is reduced. As the metal is subjected to deformation by this cold working process, it hardens and it has to be softened again by annealing at various stages between drawing operations to enable the progressive reductions to be achieved. The temper or hardness of the tube after all drawing operations have been carried out can be adjusted to suit the particular purpose for which the tube is to be used; thus "hard," "half hard" or "soft" tube can be produced by an appropriate adjustment of the final drawing operations and the annealing treatment to which the tube is subjected.

14

Most tubes are drawn in straight lengths, though longer lengths can be produced by coiling the tube on a drum, such tube usually being supplied only in the "soft" condition.

Straight and
Coiled tubes
available

Although copper tubes to British Standards are made from high quality metal, and every stage in their production is most carefully controlled, all finished tubes are subjected to searching examination and rigorous testing to ensure that they are free from defects and are fully up to the high standard guaranteed.

Every tube receives a visual examination both internally and externally, and its diameter and wall thickness are checked to ensure that they are within the exceptionally close tolerances to which the dimensions of copper tubes are specified. Samples taken from each batch of tubes are subjected also to mechanical tests; for example, all light gauge tubes supplied to British Standard 659 have to withstand being flared out at the end to a diameter at least 25% greater than their original diameter. Samples taken from the tubes are also tested for tensile strength which, in the case of "half hard" tubes to B.S. 659, must be not less than 16·5 tons per square inch. In addition to all these tests, every tube is subjected to a hydraulic pressure test which it must withstand without showing signs of leaking or distortion, the hydraulic pressure applied usually being between 500 and 1,000 lb. per square inch.

Testing and
Inspection

From the above, it will be appreciated that a copper tube to the appropriate British Standard is a high-quality product which, subject to proper installation and use, will, with certainty, give satisfactory service. Further details relating to British Standards are given in Chapter II, while all the necessary information relating to the correct manipulation, installation and use of copper tubes for all pipe-line services in building will be found in the various sections of the book which follow.

CHAPTER II

COPPER TUBES

In the British Standards for solid drawn copper tubes it is laid down that the tubes are to be either of deoxidised copper containing not less than 99·2% copper and 0·3% to 0·5% arsenic, or deoxidised non-arsenical copper containing not less than 99·85% copper.

For general building work, light gauge copper tubes have now superseded heavy gauge pipes with screwed joints. There are, however, certain cases in which these pipes are used for high pressures, or for certain industrial purposes, where it is necessary to use a "screwing size" copper tube. The sizes of such tubes are covered by B.S. 61, Part 1, 1947, Copper Tubes (Heavy Gauge) for General Purposes; whilst thread dimensions are set out in Part 2 of the same Specification. (*See* Tables I, II, and III below.) Fittings,

TABLE I—*British Standard Copper Tubes (suitable for screwed connections). For general purposes at working pressures up to and including 175 lb. per square inch. (B.S. 61, Pt. 1— 1947.)*

Nominal Size	Outside Diameter		Bore	Thickness					Weight per foot
	Maximum	Minimum		S.W.G.	Inch	Tolerance on mean thickness	Min. thickness at any point	Max. thickness at any point	
in.	in.	in.	in.		in.	in.	in.	in.	lb.
⅛	0·262	0·256	0·134	16	0·064	±0·004	0·058	0·070	0·151
¼	0·403	0·397	0·243	14	0·080	±0·006	0·070	0·090	0·310
⅜	0·528	0·522	0·368	14	0·080	±0·006	0·070	0·090	0·431
½	0·653	0·647	0·469	13	0·092	±0·006	0·082	0·102	0·621
⅝	0·781	0·773	0·597	13	0·092	±0·006	0·082	0·102	0·763
¾	0·906	0·898	0·722	13	0·092	±0·006	0·082	0·102	0·902
⅞	1·031	1·023	0·847	13	0·092	±0·006	0·082	0·102	1·041
1	1·172	1·164	0·964	12	0·104	±0·006	0·094	0·114	1·339
1¼	1·422	1·414	1·214	12	0·104	±0·006	0·094	0·114	1·654
1½	1·672	1·664	1·464	12	0·104	±0·006	0·094	0·114	1·968
1¾	1·946	1·938	1·690	10	0·128	±0·008	0·115	0·141	2·810
2	2·199	2·189	1·943	10	0·128	±0·008	0·115	0·141	3·200
2¼	2·449	2·439	2·193	10	0·128	±0·008	0·115	0·141	3·587
2½	2·699	2·689	2·411	9	0·144	±0·008	0·131	0·157	4·443
2¾	2·949	2·939	2·661	9	0·144	±0·008	0·131	0·157	4·879
3	3·223	3·213	2·935	9	0·144	±0·008	0·131	0·157	5·356
3¼	3·473	3·463	3·153	8	0·160	±0·008	0·147	0·173	6·404
3½	3·750	3·738	3·430	8	0·160	±0·008	0·147	0·173	6·939
3¾	4·000	3·988	3·680	8	0·160	±0·008	0·147	0·173	7·423
4	4·274	4·262	3·972	7	0·176	±0·008	0·163	0·189	8·714

of which there is a wide range, are of gunmetal or similar copper alloy which is resistant to corrosive influences and of adequate strength. B.S. 99, 1922, gives detailed dimensions and thread sizes for fittings to be used for this class of work. In making the joint between tube and fitting, the ideal to be aimed at is a perfectly cut thread on tube and fitting screwed up dry or with a thin coating of jointing compound. In some districts, however, it is the practice to clean, flux and tin the threads with "fine" solder and to apply heat from a blow lamp so as to maintain the solder in a fluid state while screwing the fittings home. Afterwards extra solder is floated round the mouth of the joint and to fill any spaces in the threaded portion of the joint. It is important, when cutting the thread on the tubes, not to allow the dies to run too far, otherwise a number of threads will be visible outside the fitting and of course the effective strength of the tube will be thereby somewhat reduced.

Set out on page 18 is the table of pipe threads shown in B.S. 61, Part 2, 1946.

TABLE II—*British Standard Copper Tubes (suitable for screwed connections). For general purposes at working pressures over 175 lb. per square inch up to and including 300 lb. per square inch. (B.S. 61, Part 1, 1947.)*

Nominal size	Outside Diameter		Bore	Thickness						Mean weight per foot
	Maxi-mum	Mini-mum		S.W.G.	Inch	Toler-ance on mean thick-ness	Min. thick-ness at any point	Max. thick-ness at any point		
in.	in.	in.	in.		in.	in.	in.	in.		lb.
$\frac{1}{4}$	0·393	0·387	0·249	15	0·072	±0·004	0·066	0·078		0·277
$\frac{3}{8}$	0·531	0·525	0·341	13	0·092	±0·006	0·082	0·102		0·485
$\frac{3}{8}$	0·669	0·663	0·461	12	0·104	.±0·006	0·094	0·114		0·707
$\frac{1}{2}$	0·840	0·834	0·608	11	0·116	±0·006	0·106	0·126		1·012
$\frac{5}{8}$	0·919	0·911	0·663	10	0·128	±0·008	0·115	0·141		1·219
$\frac{3}{4}$	1·058	1·050	0·802	10	0·128	±0·008	0·115	0·141		1·434
$\frac{7}{8}$	1·206	1·198	0·950	10	0·128	±0·008	0·115	0·141		1·663
1	1·328	1·320	1·040	9	0·144	±0·008	0·131	0·157		2·056
$1\frac{1}{8}$	1·509	1·501	1·189	8	0·160	±0·008	0·147	0·173		2·604
$1\frac{1}{4}$	1·669	1·661	1·349	8	0·160	±0·008	0·147	0·173		2·914
$1\frac{3}{8}$	1·762	1·754	1·442	8	0·160	±0·008	0·147	0·173		3·094
$1\frac{1}{2}$	1·901	1·893	1·549	7	0·176	±0·008	0·163	0·189		3·665
$1\frac{5}{8}$	2·099	2·091	1·747	7	0·176	±0·008	0·163	0·189		4·087
$1\frac{3}{4}$	2·133	2·125	1·781	7	0·176	±0·008	0·163	0·189		4·160
$1\frac{7}{8}$	2·264	2·254	1·912	7	0·176	±0·008	0·163	0·189		4·436
2	2·368	2·358	1·984	6	0·192	±0·008	0·179	0·205		5·043
$2\frac{1}{4}$	2·607	2·597	2·223	6	0·192	±0·008	0·179	0·205		5·599
$2\frac{1}{2}$	2·981	2·971	2·557	5	0·212	±0·010	0·197	0·227		7·092
$2\frac{3}{4}$	3·230	3·220	2·806	5	0·212	±0·010	0·197	0·227		7·729
3	3·481	3·471	3·017	4	0·232	±0·010	0·217	0·247		9·107
$3\frac{1}{4}$	3·720	3·710	3·256	4	0·232	±0·010	0·217	0·247		9·777
$3\frac{1}{2}$	3·973	3·961	3·469	3	0·252	±0·012	0·232	0·272		11·328
$3\frac{3}{4}$	4·223	4·211	3·719	3	0·252	±0·012	0·232	0·272		12·090
4	4·473	4·461	3·921	2	0·276	±0·012	0·256	0·296		13·996

TABLE III—*B.S. Pipe Threads for use on Copper Pipes.*

Nominal size of pipe	Outside diameter of copper pipe			Number of threads per inch	Nominal size of pipe	Outside diameter of copper pipe			Number of threads per inch
	Standard	Maximum	Minimum			Standard	Maximum	Minimum	
in.	in.	in.	in.		in.	in.	in.	in.	
$\frac{3}{8}$	0·666	0·669	0·663	19	2	2·363	2·368	2·358	11
$\frac{1}{2}$	0·837	0·840	0·834	14	$2\frac{1}{2}$	2·976	2·981	2·971	11
$\frac{3}{4}$	1·054	1·058	1·050	14	3	3·476	3·481	3·471	11
1	1·324	1·328	1·320	11	$3\frac{1}{2}$	3·967	3·973	3·961	11
$1\frac{1}{4}$	1·665	1·669	1·661	11	4	4·467	4·473	4·461	11
$1\frac{1}{2}$	1·897	1·901	1·893	11					

TABLE IV—*British Standard Light Gauge Copper Tubes for Water and Gas, suitable for the following working water pressures: $\frac{1}{8}$ in. to 2 in. nominal size inclusive, 200 lb. per square inch (460 ft. head of water); $2\frac{1}{2}$ in. to 4 in., 150 lb. per square inch (350 ft. head of water); 5 in. to 6 in., 100 lb. per square inch; or higher at the discretion of the user. (B.S. 659–1955 and B.S. 1401–1947.)*

Nominal size	Outside Diameter		Bore	Thickness		Tolerance on thickness		Standard weight per foot
	Standard (maximum)	Minimum		S.W.G.	Inch	Plus	Minus	
in.	in.	in.	in.		in.	in.	in.	lb.
$\frac{1}{8}$	0·205	0·202	0·149	22	0·028	0·003	0·003	0·06
$\frac{3}{16}$	0·283	0·280	0·219	21	0·032	0·003	0·003	0·097
$\frac{1}{4}$	0·346	0·343	0·274	20	0·036	0·003	0·003	0·135
$\frac{3}{8}$	0·471	0·468	0·399	20	0·036	0·003	0·003	0·19
$\frac{1}{2}$	0·596	0·593	0·516	19	0·040	0·003	0·003	0·27
$\frac{3}{4}$	0·846	0·843	0·766	19	0·040	0·003	0·003	0·39
1	1·112	1·109	1·016	18	0·048	0·004	0·004	0·62
$1\frac{1}{4}$	1·362	1·359	1·266	18	0·048	0·004	0·004	0·76
$1\frac{1}{2}$	1·612	1·609	1·516	18	0·048	0·004	0·004	0·91
2	2·128	2·125	2·016	17	0·056	0·004	0·004	1·40
$2\frac{1}{2}$	2·628	2·622	2·516	17	0·056	0·004	0·004	1·74
3	3·144	3·138	3·016	16	0·064	0·004	0·004	2·38
$3\frac{1}{2}$	3·660	3·654	3·516	15	0·072	0·005	0·005	3·12
4	4·184	4·178	4·024	14	0·080	0·006	0·006	3·97
5	5·125	5·115	4·941	13	0·092	0·006	0·006	5·60
6	6·125	6·113	5·917	12	0·104	0·006	0·006	7·58

LIGHT GAUGE COPPER TUBES

The present widespread use of copper for all forms of pipework and conduit in building is largely a result of the development of suitable means of jointing light gauge tubes. The joints commonly used to-day are manipulative and non-manipulative compression fittings, capillary soldered joints and joints made by hard or silver solder and welding processes. The first type of joint used was a compression joint employing a rubber ring, but this was not very satisfactory and was soon superseded by the fixed cone joint, where the fitting had a coned projection machined at the end and the tube was expanded and coupled to it by the action of tightening the nut. Improvements were constantly being made by the manufacturers until to-day there is a large variety of joints available; see Chapter III, "Jointing of Light Gauge Copper Tubes," page 21.

For many years the requirements as to gauge or wall thickness of tubes differed widely under the regulations of the various local authorities, but to-day, light gauge copper tubing having proved itself, every authority accepts the sizes and gauges laid down by B.S. 659, 1955, for services above ground and to B.S. 1386, 1947, for tubes to be buried underground. Under these Specifications, copper tubes up to 2 in. nominal size are allowed for use with working pressures up to 200 lb. per square inch (460 feet head), 150 lb. per square inch (350 feet head) for tubes from 2½ in. to 4 in., and 100 lb. per square inch (230 feet head) for 5 in. and 6 in. tubes.

It will be noted that the allowable pressures or working heads are such that under normal conditions the limits imposed are never likely to be exceeded. However, a glance at the theoretical bursting pressures tabulated on p. 123 will assure readers that even when

TABLE V—*Light Gauge Copper Tubes for Sanitation Purposes.*
(*British Standard* 659–1955.)

Nominal Size	Outside Diameter		Bore	Thickness		Tolerance on Thickness		Standard Weight per Foot
	Standard (Maximum)	Minimum		S.W.G.	Inch	Plus	Minus	
in.	in.	in.	in.		in.	in.	in.	lb.
1	1·112	1·109	1·016	18	0·048	0·004	0·004	0·62
1¼	1·362	1·359	1·266	18	0·048	0·004	0·004	0·76
1½	1·612	1·609	1·516	18	0·048	0·004	0·004	0·91
2	2·128	2·125	2·032	18	0·048	0·004	0·004	1·21
2½	2·628	2·622	2·532	18	0·048	0·004	0·004	1·50
3	3·144	3·138	3·032	17	0·056	0·004	0·004	2·09
3½	3·660	3·654	3·548	17	0·056	0·004	0·004	2·44
4	4·184	4·178	4·056	16	0·064	0·004	0·004	3·19
5	5·125	5·115	4·997	16	0·064	0·004	0·004	3·92
6	6·125	6·115	5·981	15	0·072	0·005	0·005	5·27

working at 200 lb. per square inch, there is a large margin before the tubes will come within the bursting pressure range.

In addition, B.S. 659, 1955 also covers tubes for sanitation purposes and reference should be made to pp. 18-20, where tables from these specifications are reproduced.

It should be noted that the outside diameters of corresponding tube sizes as stated in B.S. 1386, 1947 are the same; this enables any standard compression or capillary fitting to be used with tubes made to either Standard.

TABLE VI—*Copper Tubes to be Buried Underground.*
(*British Standard* 1386–1947.)

Nominal Size	Outside Diameter		Bore	Thickness					
	Maximum	Minimum		S.W.G.	Inch	Tolerance on Mean Thickness	Min. Thickness at Any Point	Max. Thickness at Any Point	Mean Weight per Foot
in.	in.	in.	in.		in.	in.	in.	in.	lb.
$\frac{1}{8}$	0·205	0·202	0·125	19	0·040	±0·004	0·034	0·046	0·080
$\frac{3}{16}$	0·283	0·280	0·203	19	0·040	±0·004	0·034	0·046	0·118
$\frac{1}{4}$	0·346	0·343	0·250	18	0·048	±0·004	0·042	0·054	0·174
$\frac{3}{8}$	0·471	0·468	0·375	18	0·048	±0·004	0·042	0·054	0·246
$\frac{1}{2}$	0·596	0·593	0·500	18	0·048	±0·004	0·042	0·054	0·319
$\frac{3}{4}$	0·846	0·843	0·734	17	0·056	±0·004	0·050	0·062	0·536
1	1·112	1·109	0·984	16	0·064	±0·004	0·058	0·070	0·812
$1\frac{1}{4}$	1·362	1·359	1·234	16	0·064	±0·004	0·058	0·070	1·006
$1\frac{1}{2}$	1·612	1·609	1·468	15	0·072	±0·004	0·066	0·078	1·342
2	2·128	2·125	1·968	14	0·080	±0·006	0·070	0·090	1·983
$2\frac{1}{2}$	2·628	2·622	2·444	13	0·092	±0·006	0·082	0·102	2·824
3	3·144	3·138	2·936	12	0·104	±0·006	0·094	0·114	3·826
$3\frac{1}{2}$	3·660	3·654	3·428	11	0·116	±0·006	0·106	0·126	4·975
4	4·184	4·178	3·928	10	0·128	±0·008	0·115	0·141	6·282

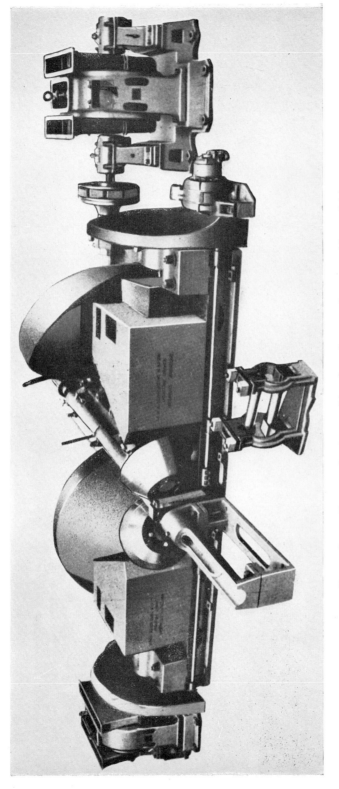

PLATE I.   *Rotary piercing machine for tube manufacture.*   (*See p.* 14.)

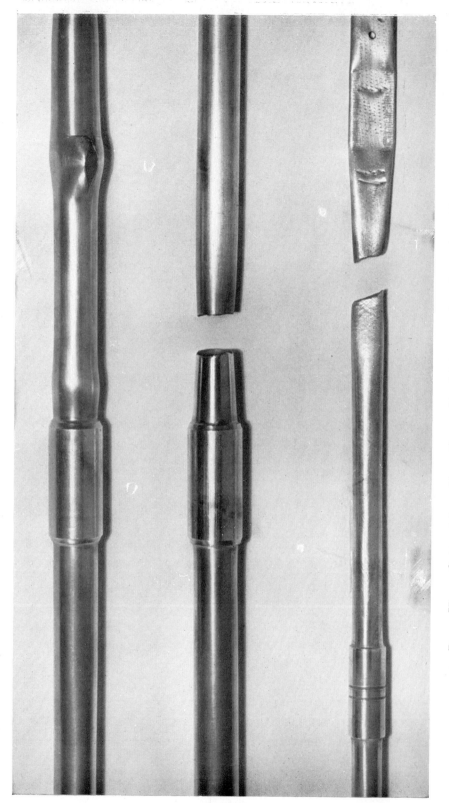

PLATE II. *Copper tubes with capillary soldered joints, tested to destruction. (See p. 28.)*

CHAPTER III

JOINTING OF LIGHT GAUGE COPPER TUBES

As stated in the previous Chapter, there are three main forms of jointing for light gauge tubes, namely, (*a*) compression joints, (*b*) capillary soldered joints, and (*c*) silver or hard soldering and welding. In addition, light gauge tubes are occasionally furnace brazed using a spelter filler, but this method is only suitable for bench work.

British Standard 864, 1953, "Capillary Fittings and Compression Fittings of Copper and Copper Alloy, for Use with Light Gauge Copper Tube," gives the general dimensions and classifies them as non-manipulative compression fittings Type A, manipulative compression fittings Type B, and capillary soldered fittings, and states that the fittings shall be of copper or a suitable corrosion-resisting copper alloy; a Table sets out the allowable hydraulic working pressures and temperatures for these forms of joints, but it may be of interest to the reader that many of the fittings, both capillary and compression, can be, and in fact are, sometimes used at higher temperatures and pressures and also for low-pressure steam services. Under such conditions, however, the manufacturers should be consulted regarding any special requirements necessary to ensure their products giving satisfactory service. In connection with the foregoing, a glance at Plate II opposite will give some idea of the strength of the joints illustrated. **British Standard Fittings**

In the past, some confusion has arisen over the method of stating sizes of tees or crosses. To overcome this, a standard method has now been adopted by all manufacturers as follows:— **Ordering Fittings**

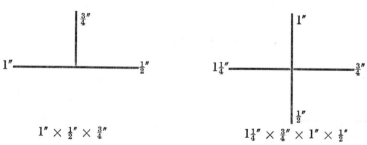

$1'' \times \frac{1}{2}'' \times \frac{3}{4}''$ $\qquad\qquad$ $1\frac{1}{4}'' \times \frac{3}{4}'' \times 1'' \times \frac{1}{2}''$

Fig. 1. *Method of numbering ends when ordering fittings.*

A good type of joint should not in any way restrict the bore of the tube and in addition should preferably be so made as to allow of easy dismantling for maintenance or other purposes.

To-day, when many large all-copper installations are being erected, it is common

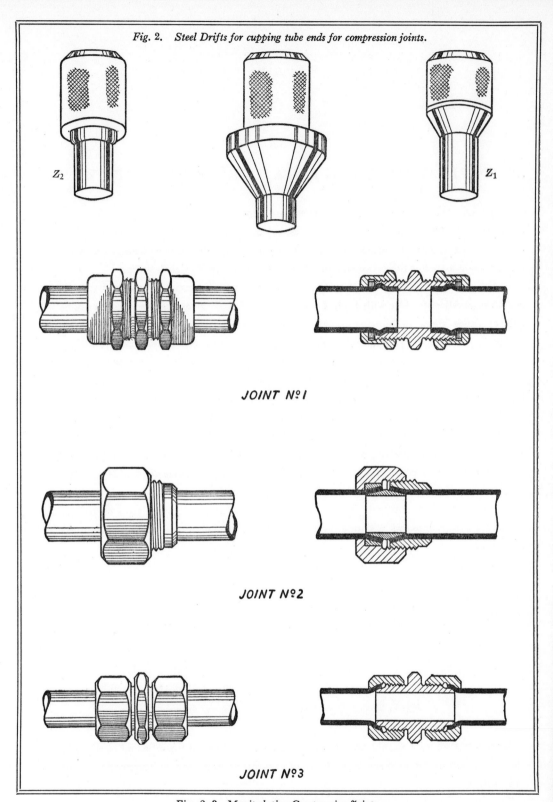

Fig. 2. Steel Drifts for cupping tube ends for compression joints.

Z_2

Z_1

JOINT № 1

JOINT № 2

JOINT № 3

Figs. 2, 3. Manipulative Compression Joints.

22

practice to use flanges instead of coupling nuts on compression joints above 2 in., but apart from this variation the principle of the joint remains the same.

COMPRESSION JOINTS

The non-manipulative type of compression joint, as its name implies, does not require any working of the tube end other than cutting square. The joint is made tight by means of a loose ring or sleeve which grips the outside wall of the tube when the coupling nut is tightened. **Types of Compression Joints**

In the manipulative type of compression joint the end of the tube is flared, cupped or belled with special forming tools and is compressed by means of a coupling nut against a shaped end of corresponding section on the fitting or a loose thimble. (See Plate XVI, page 96.)

A rather different type of manipulative compression joint is one in which a special tool (Fig. 3a) is used to roll a bead on the tube about half an inch from the end. When the coupling nut is tightened, the bead is compressed against the mouth of the fitting and so makes a fluid- and gas-tight joint.

Fig. 4 shows typical joints of the non-manipulative type. A joint of this type is made by simply slipping the coupling nut and compression ring on to the squared end of the tube and inserting it into the mouth of the fitting up to the internal shoulder. The coupling nut is then screwed up tight with a spanner, causing the edge, or edges, of the compression ring to bite into the copper tube. The effect is shown in exaggerated form on the right of Fig. 4. **Making Non-Manipulative Compression Joints**

Fig. 3 illustrates the three main types of manipulative compression joints. Joint No. 1 is prepared by cutting the tube to length, squaring off the end and after slipping the coupling nut on, the special expanding tool shown in Fig. 3a is inserted into the tube. **Making Manipulative Compression Joints**

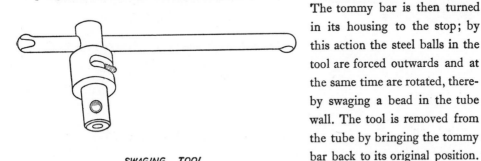

SWAGING TOOL

Fig. 3a.

The tommy bar is then turned in its housing to the stop; by this action the steel balls in the tool are forced outwards and at the same time are rotated, thereby swaging a bead in the tube wall. The tool is removed from the tube by bringing the tommy bar back to its original position. The tube is then inserted in the mouth of the fitting and the joint completed by screwing up the coupling nut.

In joint No. 2, the centre ferrule or olive is machined from copper, bronze or brass and the angle or degree of taper matches that formed on the tube end after it has been expanded by the steel drift. The mouth of the male portion of the fitting and the

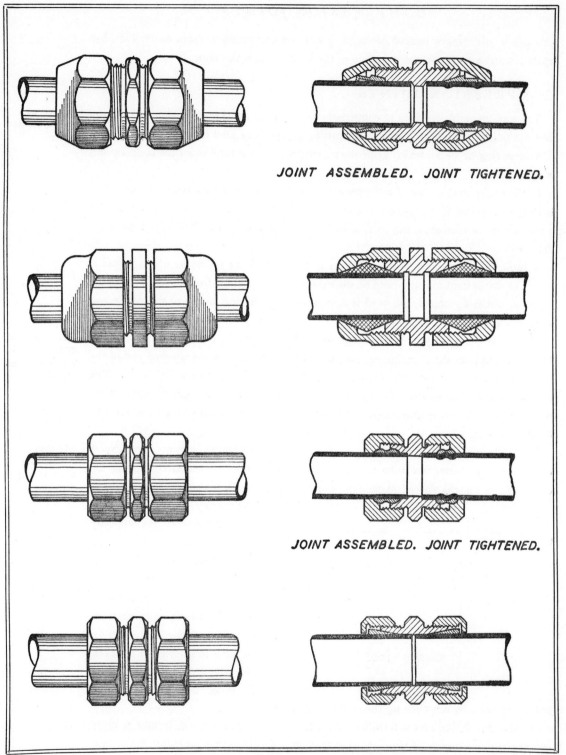

JOINT ASSEMBLED. JOINT TIGHTENED.

JOINT ASSEMBLED. JOINT TIGHTENED.

Fig. 4. Non-Manipulative Compression Joints.

24

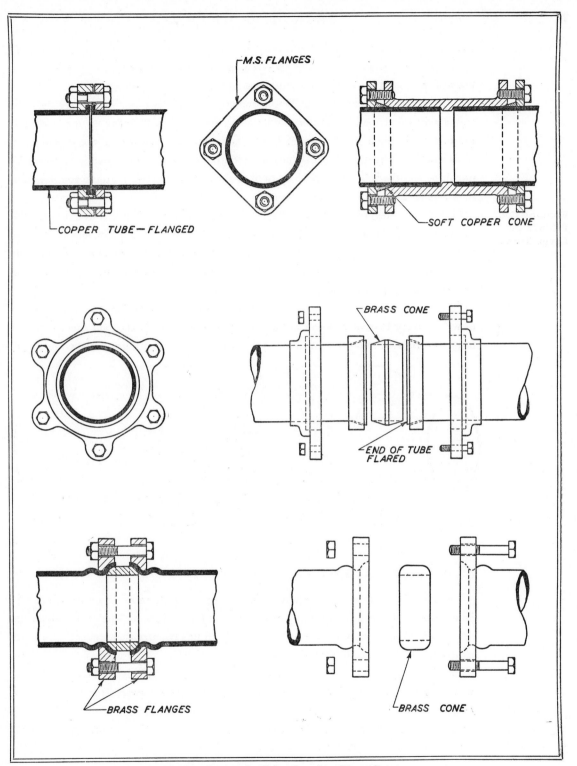

Fig. 5. *Compression Joints for tubes of large diameter.*

friction ring inside the coupling nut are similarly machined, so that the jointing faces all marry up. The union is assembled by screwing up the coupling nut with a spanner, the body of the fitting being held at the same time with a second spanner.

In preparing and making joint No. 3, the coupling nut is first slipped over the tube end, a split collar die is placed on the tube and secured by tightening up the side nuts; the tube end is then opened by the drift Z^1 and after withdrawing this the second drift, Z^2 is used to form the belled or cupped mouth as shown. The collar is removed by unbolting and the tube end pulled up tight to the body by screwing up the coupling nut, thus making a mechanically sound joint.

Compression Fittings for Large Tubes

Fig. 5 indicates types of compression joints suitable for large tubes up to and including 8 in. diameter. These joints are entirely satisfactory for hot and cold water services and heating work, but must not be used for soil pipes as the tees and bends are not angled or swept. For soil pipes, bends and branch joints may be fabricated from copper tube, or special weldable fittings may be used.

For high-pressure water or steam installations, the general practice is to hard solder or weld standard circular gunmetal flanges on to the tube ends and bolt them together, using a corrugated brass or composition joint ring between the flanges as shown in Fig. 6.

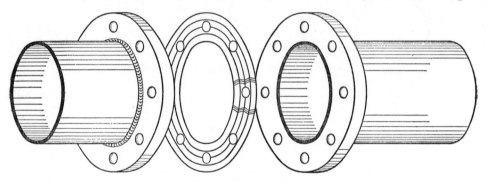

Fig. 6.   Flanged Joint.

CAPILLARY SOLDERED JOINTS

The use of "soldered" or "sweated" joints, more properly called "capillary soldered" joints, was originally developed in America and on the Continent. The development has since been taken up on such a considerable scale in this country that almost every water authority now accepts this economical and neat type of joint (Fig. 7, p. 27. See also Plate XXVIII, p. 121.) Thus, capillary fittings are being increasingly used for hot and cold water services, heating installations, waste and ventilating pipes (for which special fittings are obtainable) and steam lines up to 6 in. in diameter.

Manufacture of Capillary Fittings

Capillary fittings are made from copper and copper alloys. Copper fittings are usually cold wrought from copper tube or sheet or may be made by electrodeposition. Wrought fittings are strong and neat and free from the possibility of porosity.

Copper alloy fittings are made by casting or hot pressing. The latter are said to be more free from possible porosity, though in some areas they may suffer from dezincification and in these areas a cast gunmetal or wrought copper fitting should be used.

Although not usually required with capillary fittings, it should be noted that copper fittings can, if necessary be welded or brazed.

Capillary joints should not be confused with the old-fashioned soldered union. They are constructed upon the basic principle of capillary attraction, which provides the means by which molten solder is drawn into the narrow space between the two closely fitting

General Principles of Capillary Joints

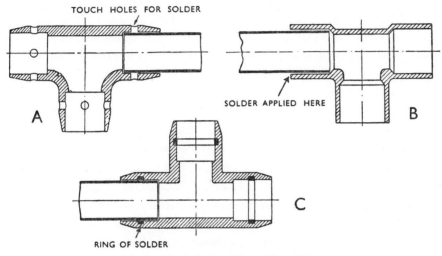

Fig. 7. Typical soft solder capillary fittings.

metal surfaces of the exterior of the tube ends and the interior of the jointing piece. The joint can be made in either a horizontal or vertical position. The closeness of the fit is the major factor in ensuring capillarity, and it is therefore of the greatest importance that the fittings are those intended for the exact gauges and diameters of the tubes being used.

The certainty of an exact fit is provided for by the British Standard for Light Gauge Copper Tubes (No. 659, 1955, see Tables IV, V, pp. 18, 19), which specifies both wall thicknesses and external diameters and states the permissible tolerances; and is still further assured by British Standard 864, 1953, "Capillary Fittings and Compression Fittings for Use with Light Gauge Copper Tubes," which similarly specifies the dimensions of fittings.

When capillary fittings were first introduced into this country, it was suggested that there might be a likelihood of corrosion due to electrolytic action taking place between the copper of the tubes or fittings and the jointing solder. Experience, however, has proved that this fear was unfounded, for it is most unlikely that any appreciable action could take place with normal waters and a properly made joint, since the amount of

Corrosion Resistance

solder left exposed to the action of the water inside the pipe, or to condensation on the outside, is so small as to be negligible. If the water is likely to be of such a corrosive nature that there is a danger of electrolytic action, it may be assumed that it is sufficiently corrosive to act upon plain metal and should, therefore, be submitted to preliminary examination, no matter what type of joint is used.

Resistance to Thermal Stresses

Another point which was given considerable attention in the early days of capillary fittings was their resistance to the stresses likely to be encountered in hot water and heating installations, particularly where long runs of pipe were involved; the argument being that the stresses which would be set up by the continual pull-and-push action caused by the variations in temperature, combined with the reduction in the strength of soft solder at the boiling temperature of water, might, in certain conditions, cause the failure of the joint. Extensive laboratory tests for strength in torsion, in shear and under hydraulic pressure, gave completely satisfactory results. Plate II (facing p. 21) illustrates made joints tested to destruction by tensile and hydraulic tests. Furthermore, in ordinary building work, conditions such as those just described are most unlikely to set up dangerous stresses, since pipe runs are comparatively short, and in any case frequent changes in direction of a pipe by bends and offsets allow slight movements which reduce the stresses. Moreover, years of experience have now proved that capillary joints are perfectly satisfactory for hot water and heating installations. Where especially long pipe runs are encountered in such installations, provision should of course be made to take up the movement due to temperature variations, by means of expansion bends or expansion joints. Stresses due to thermal expansion and contraction are undesirable, whatever the jointing method, as some part of the installation will be obliged to accommodate them.

Resistance to Vibration

Laboratory tests, which were carried out to discover whether the soft solder joint in a capillary fitting would break down in conditions where excessive vibration was met with, proved that such failure was not likely to occur. Subsequent large-scale use of this type of joint in railway rolling stock, on machines, and in other places where excessive vibration is encountered, has wholly upheld the laboratory results. Under specially severe conditions a silver solder is sometimes used as an added safeguard in making the joint, and there are now available capillary joints suitable for use with such solder, which are recommended for use under special conditions and also where high temperatures, such as on steam lines, are encountered.

Assembly of Joints

The assembly of any type of capillary joint consists, briefly, of cutting square the tube ends, thoroughly cleaning them and the inside of the fitting, fluxing, inserting the tubes into the fitting, and heating with a blowlamp. When the heat is applied, solder is fed into the joint from solder wire applied (*a*) at a touch hole in the fitting, (*b*) at the mouth of the fitting, or (*c*) from a reservoir of solder already within the fitting (Fig. 7). As an alternative to feeding in solder by these means, the joint can be made with solder paint, applied evenly to the tube after cleaning and prior to insertion into the fitting.

(1) *Prepare the copper tube to be jointed by cleaning with steel wool. Be sure that all traces of oxidation are removed. Parts should be bright copper colour.*

(2) *Apply an even coat of non-corrosive flux.*

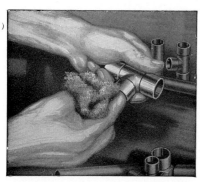

(3) *Clean the sockets of the fitting with steel wool to remove all traces of oxidation.*

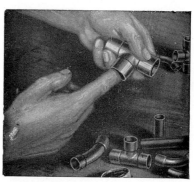

(4) *Apply an even coat of flux inside the sockets.*

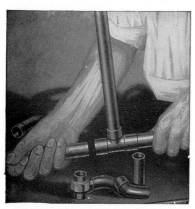

(5) *Slip the tubes into the fittings and see that they are bedded squarely on the shoulders of the sockets.*

(6) *Apply blowlamp. When the flux begins to boil, test by touching edge of fitting with solder wire. If hot enough, solder will melt and flow, filling cavity between wall of tube and fitting almost instantly.*

PLATE III.   *Making a joint in light gauge copper tubing with a capillary fitting.*
(*Type* B, *see p.* 27.)

PLATE IV. *Annealing a light gauge copper tube before bending.* (*See p.* 43)

Although each step in assembling is in itself a simple operation, too much stress cannot be laid on thoroughness, and it is therefore thought advisable to explain each stage in greater detail.

(1) The tube must be sawn off square to bed evenly upon the shoulder at the bottom of the socket, and all rough edges formed by the sawing operation should be removed by file or reamer. For sawing, a special vice is obtainable which has interchangeable jaws to hold tubes of all sizes from ½ in. to 2 in. This vice holds any length of tube, and it is claimed that because the saw-blade moves between close guides there is less burr to be removed and no trueing up is required after the cut is made. There are also available tube cutters which ensure that the tube end is cut square; these can easily be carried in one's pocket. After cutting to length, the tube end must be true and round, and its shape must be corrected if necessary.

(2) The exterior surface of the tube at its ends, and the interior surface of the fitting, must be thoroughly scoured to remove all traces of dirt and oxide, which would prevent the solder from adhering to the metal. This operation may be carried out with steel wool or sandpaper and must be particularly thorough. Emery paper or emery cloth must not be used.

(3) The metal surfaces to be united on both tube and fitting are next evenly coated with flux to prevent the surfaces oxidising when heat is applied. It is important that the flux used should be supplied, or be approved by, the manufacturer of the fittings.

(4) The tube ends are then inserted in the fitting, and it is important to ensure that the tubes are lined up accurately, and that their ends bed squarely on the socket shoulders.

(5) Heat is applied by playing the flame of a blowlamp upon the outside of the socket until it has reached an even temperature all round sufficient to melt the solder easily. This temperature may be determined, when applying the solder externally (Fig. 7, A and B), by watching for flux vapours. When these appear, it is time to apply the solder at the touch-hole (Type A) or at the mouth of the socket (Type B). The socket should not be over-heated, as over-heating may break down the flux and burn the solder, and may also oxidise the cleaned surfaces. If in Type A the solder does not run freely into the touch-hole and does not appear at the mouth of the socket, or in Type B does not disappear freely into the socket before it finally floods up to the mouth, the joint should be regarded with suspicion and it would be advisable to remake it.

When using Type C, it is only necessary to apply heat after having performed carefully the operations of cleaning, fluxing, etc. The joint should be closely observed to see that the solder creeps out to the mouth of the socket and forms a complete ring of solder. Plate III (facing p. 28) shows the various stages in the making of a capillary joint.

The following soft solders are widely used with capillary fittings:

(1) 50% tin, 50% lead (melting range 185° C. to 215° C.). This is used for operating temperatures up to 250° F., or 15 lb. per square inch saturated steam pressure.

Soft Solders

(2) 39% tin, 60% lead, 1% antimony (melting range 185° C. to 230° C.). This is used

for saturated steam pressures up to 50 lb. per square inch and for water pressures up to 300 lb. per square inch.

(3) 95% tin, 5% antimony (melting range 235° C. to 240° C.). This solder has greater strength than either (1) or (2) at temperatures in the neighbourhood of the boiling point of water. It may be used in certain instances for saturated steam pressures up to 75 lb. per square inch, and for high pressure refrigeration lines.

Strength of Solders and Soldered Joints

The strength of a soldered joint depends upon the actual strength and ductility of the solder rather than upon the tendency of the solder, when melted, to become alloyed with the copper or brass of the parts to be joined. Pure tin alloys readily with the copper parts, but although additions of lead and/or antimony to the tin reduce the alloying action, it has been shown that the strength of the solder is increased by these additions.

The strength of a capillary soldered joint depends upon the strength of the solder in shear, and it has been found that the maximum shear strength of a tin-lead solder is obtained when the tin and lead are in the proportions of 63% and 37% respectively. (This alloy has a melting point of 183° C. and no melting range.) In practice, however, the maximum strength of soldered joints is not obtained with the solder having the maximum shear strength, but with a solder which is rather richer in lead, having a lead content of approximately 53% (nearly the familiar 50/50 solder). It is said that the probable reason for this is that when the joint cools the solder is subjected to stresses due to contraction and that a solder rich in lead, having greater ductility, will more readily adapt itself to such stresses.

It is because of their lack of ductility and restricted melting range, which does not allow easy manipulation, that solders of which the compositions approximate to the 63% tin, 37% lead alloy, such as the Grade A solder of B.S. 219, 1949 (65% tin, 34% lead, 1% antimony), are not generally used for plumbing work in spite of their strength. Solders (1) and (2) above are therefore recommended for capillary joints, because they possess reasonably high strength and ductility, while being at the same time economical in cost on account of their comparatively low tin content.

The addition of small amounts of antimony (up to 6% of the tin content) has the effect of further increasing the strength of the tin-lead solders. The strengthening effect of antimony increases progressively with the tin content, the greatest increase of strength being obtained when there is no lead present; the 95% tin, 5% antimony solder (No. 3, above), has a shear strength approximately double that of pure tin. On account of its high tin content this solder is more expensive than the others mentioned, but because it possesses considerable ductility and strength and a comparatively high melting range, enabling it to maintain its strength at temperatures in the neighbourhood of, or above, the boiling point of water, it is particularly suitable for high-class work or for work in which comparatively high temperatures and shear stresses are likely.

It may be of interest to mention here that it is claimed that a solder composed only of tin and silver, which, on account of its low melting point of 235° C. (compared with melting points in the region of 600° C. to 850° C. of copper-zinc-silver solders), may be classed as a soft solder, is especially suitable for corrosive conditions and for intermittent immersion in water, such as for the soldered seams of copper balls.

Most of the makers of soldered joints recommend the use of a non-acid flux such as resin. Resin-cored solder wire is also used. Another typical composition consists of zinc chloride with some ammonium chloride mixed in a stiff petroleum jelly, but fluxes of this type, which tend to be acid in reaction, should be carefully wiped off when soldering is completed. **Fluxes for Soft Soldering**

SILVER SOLDERING, BRAZING, BRONZE WELDING AND COPPER WELDING

Before describing in detail the jointing of copper tubes by these methods, it is thought expedient to describe each process in general terms and so to avoid any confusion which the apparent similarity of technique might cause in the mind of a reader.

The principal differences in technique between hard soldering, brazing or welding and the soft soldered capillary jointing already described, arise from the much higher temperatures necessary to melt the jointing materials used (silver solders, brazing spelters and copper or bronze filler rods. The table overleaf may be taken as an approximate guide to the temperatures required to melt these jointing materials.)

By selecting a suitable copper alloy filler rod instead of a copper rod, it is possible with oxy-acetylene welding technique to "bronze weld" or braze copper, or even some of the brasses, without serious risk of destructively fusing the metal of the work. The melting point of copper (1083° C.) is depressed more or less progressively by zinc additions until the melting point of the 50/50 copper-zinc alloy, used as a brazing solder, is reached. This is about 860° C.; still lower melting points are obtained by adding silver, sometimes with phosphorus, to form silver solders. The terms "hard soldering" and "brazing" are used to cover jointing operations in which the solder is either a silver solder (usually a copper-zinc-silver alloy) or a brazing spelter (brass, i.e. copper-zinc alloy).

Silver Soldering. The technique of silver soldering in the jointing of copper pipes is similar to that employed with soft solders, with the exception of the temperature and method of application of heat. Capillarity can play an important part in the making of the joint, whether a fitting is used or whether a spigot-and-socket joint is formed from the pipe ends. **General Description of Processes**

Brazing. Comparatively large areas of the work are heated to a temperature which is considerably higher than for silver soldering and yet still well below the melting point of copper. The brass jointing material melts and flows over the whole area of the surfaces to be joined and, as in silver soldering, capillarity is a major factor in the making of a successful union in pipe work.

Bronze Welding. The introduction of so-called bronze welding simplified the operative's task when compared with the degree of skill required for autogenous welding.

The process lies between brazing and autogenous welding, in so far as the filler rod is similar to brazing metal and the flame technique is comparable to that used in welding, except that there is no fusion of the base metal. Using a filler rod of silicon brass, requiring a lower flame temperature and more localised in its application, the operator

TABLE VII—*Melting Temperatures of Jointing Materials and Metals*

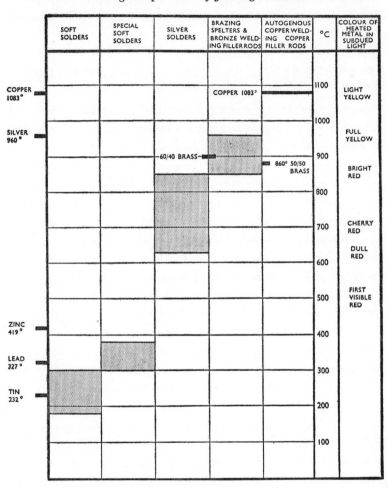

can concentrate his attention on the joint without having constantly to guard against destructive fusion of the parent metal. In making a bronze weld, the filler metal is applied in successive beads, each one running into its predecessor until the whole circumference of the joint is covered.

A further step in the direction of simplification of gas flame welding has been achieved with the introduction of the copper-phosphorus filler rod. This type of filler rod has a much lower melting point (705° C.) than even the silicon brass and it flows better, thereby making it very suitable for all classes of copper pipe work where the surfaces to be joined together can be fabricated to form a capillary space.

Autogenous or Copper Welding. Here the jointing material is of the same basic composition as the copper pipes, and the joint is made by fusing the pipe ends together by means of an oxy-acetylene flame, either with or without a copper filler rod, so that the metal of the joint and pipe is homogeneous. Owing to the high temperature required and the high thermal conductivity of copper, the areas adjacent to the joint are usually preheated, as this allows greater control over the local fusion of the actual weld.

Making Silver Soldered Joints. Generally, the use of silver solder is confined to jointing pipes not larger than 2 in. diameter, on account of the somewhat high cost of the filler. There is, however, no practical reason why it should not be used on larger pipes if so desired.

Plate XXV*a* facing p. 112 shows a range of lavatory basin wastes and vents jointed with silver solder, and a description of the work is given in the chapter on Sanitation (see p. 107).

Silver Solders

Silver solders have a basic composition of copper and silver in varying proportions (2% to 80% of silver), and may also contain zinc, cadmium or phosphorus.

The effect of adding silver to copper or to a copper-zinc alloy is that the joint attains a higher strength.

The advantage of such solders is particularly manifested in the jointing of brass to brass or copper to brass, where the brasswork is of a fragile or intricate nature. In such cases, the closeness of the melting point of a brazing spelter (copper-zinc alloy) to that of the brasswork would present a danger of the brasswork becoming damaged by the fusion of its metal. The use of a suitable silver solder, although more expensive, obviates this danger.

Silver solders are obtained in small sheets, and in strips, wire or in rods. The small sheets may be cut into widths to suit the work in hand, and strips about $\frac{1}{4}$ in. wide are usually found suitable for small pipework. To use up the strip to its end, and for convenience in handling, it may be held in a slot cut in an iron rod.

Fluxes for Silver Soldering

A flux should be used to protect the joint surfaces from oxidation, and borax in powder form or a borax mixture is suitable. This is sprinkled on when the joint is at a dull red heat. Alternatively, a saturated solution of borax dissolved in hot water may be used, which should be applied hot. If this solution is inclined to run off at the joint, the addition of up to 50% of boric acid provides greater viscosity and adherence, but raises the melting point of the flux. There are also proprietary brands of paste flux, which are claimed to be more economical and more easily applied than the powder and solutions described above. If a paste flux is employed, it is important to ensure that it is really suitable for the work in hand. An even coating of a flux solution is often obtained on the metal more easily by the use of a brush than by sprinkling or dipping.

c

**Silver
Soldered
Capillary
Fittings**

Copper and brass capillary fittings, already described for use with soft solders, may also form the means of jointing with suitable silver solders, where greater strength is required to withstand high stresses or vibration, or where a very high standard of material is desired. The use of capillary fittings reduces manual preparation of the joint, and their closeness of fit also reduces the amount of silver solder necessary, which is worth consideration with an expensive solder.

The procedure of preparing, assembling and making the joint is the same as with soft solders, with the exception of the flux and the method of applying the greater amount of heat required. The same importance should be attached to thoroughness in cleaning the fitting and pipe ends.

**Jointing by
Forming a
Socket in
the Tube**

Another method of jointing copper pipes with silver solders is to expand the end of one tube to form a socket in which the spigot end of the other tube makes a tight driving fit. The socket may be formed by means of a steel drift or by the special "tube expanders" shown in Fig. 8, A and B. Branch joints should be so prepared that a socket is formed

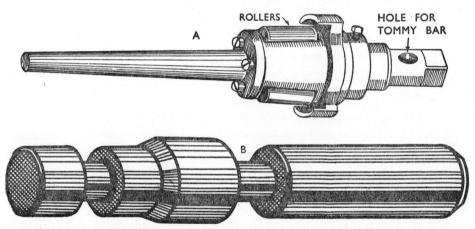

Fig. 8.   Patent tools for forming parallel sockets on tube ends.

on the main to receive the branch. This socket has to be tafted out and trued up by hand. For a pitched joint, as required in sanitary work, and sometimes in heating work, the socket is of course elliptical in shape and the branch end must be cut obliquely to the main pipe-line, care being taken that it does not project inside the crown of the main.

**Heating for
Silver
Soldering**

The greater temperature required for silver soldering necessitates the use of more powerful apparatus than the ordinary small blowlamp used for soft soldering; and for joints made in the shop, heat may be applied from a gas blowpipe with air blast, or from a small welding set.

For work *in situ*, where a supply of gas is available, an oxy-coal-gas blowpipe is a convenient means of heating, or any oxy-acetylene blowpipe can also be used, but the flame should be kept soft and the luminous cone should not be allowed too near the metal, in order to avoid local overheating.

Assuming that the flux is of powdered borax, the joint should be brought to a dull red heat, and as this is done the powder should be sprinkled on occasionally from an iron spoon, which can be conveniently formed from a piece of flattened iron wire. When the flux is quite fluid, the solder should be applied to the edge of the socket and, if proper precautions have been taken in the preparations, the solder will sink in and flood up to the mouth of the socket of the capillary fitting or the expanded tube end, whichever is used.

Making Brazed Joints. Brazing is not quite so manageable as silver soldering and calls for considerable judgment of the high temperatures which are necessary to melt the brass or brazing spelter, and which may be only a little below the melting point of the brass of fittings to which the copper tube may have to be brazed. Brass tends to become fragile at temperatures in the neighbourhood of its melting point, and damage to brass fittings may occur if the work is overheated.

Some years ago the brazing of copper tubes was considerably developed in Belgium, where light gauge tubes for water services, heating, etc., were commonly jointed by this means. Special drifts for quickly forming sockets and reductions were placed on the market at low cost, and special tools for making tee sockets for branches at various angles have also been invented. The brazing is executed by means of oxy-acetylene blow-pipes, a paste flux, and a spelter rod having a melting point of about 850° C. It is claimed that the method is economical in materials and labour and provides very strong, neat and reliable joints.

Brazing solders or spelters are of brass (copper-zinc alloy), and have melting points ranging approximately between 850° C. and 960° C. They may be obtained in rods or wire, or in granular form. British Standard 1845–1952 lays down the composition of three grades of brazing solder, as follows:—

TABLE VIII—*Nominal Composition of Brazing Solders.*

Type No.	Copper	Zinc	Melting Range
	%	%	
10	61	39	885–890° C.
9	55	45	870–880° C.
8	51	49	860–870° C.

Grade 10 is intended primarily for solder supplied in the form of slittings or wire, while Grades 9 and 8 refer more particularly to granular solder. The solder used for brazing light gauge copper, brass, and bronze should be of Grades 9 and 8 on account of their lower melting points. These are sometimes referred to as "fine," while the terms "coarse" and "hard" are applied to the solders which melt at a higher temperature.

**Preparation
of the Joint
for Brazing**

Granular solder may be obtained ready mixed with a borax flux powder. The borax fluxes used for brazing are similar to those already described for silver soldering.

Spigot-and-socket joints are formed by the same methods as described for silver soldering. The closeness of fit is not quite so important when using brazing spelter because the solder is not so expensive, but a close fit ensures capillarity as an aid to the even flow of the spelter over the area of the socket. A "drive on" fit also has the advantage of enabling the two lengths of pipe, or the pipe and fitting to which it is brazed, to be held rigidly while brazing is taking place. A loose fit necessitates holding the two parts in correct alignment with iron wires, which must be arranged clear of the actual joint. The same importance as in soft soldering should be attached to thoroughness in the cleaning of the parts to be joined together.

**Application
of Heat for
Brazing**

An ordinary blowlamp flame does not supply enough heat for brazing properly, though by arranging refractory guards of firebrick, asbestos sheet, etc., it is possible to make small brazed joints with a brazier's powerful blowlamp. The easiest means of heating in a shop is a gas blowpipe used in conjunction with a hearth of firebrick broken to about the size of walnuts. A brazier's blowlamp may be found useful in supplementing the heat from a gas forge when the work is large. An oxy-acetylene welding blowpipe can also be used and is particularly suitable for work *in situ*. A comparatively large nozzle should be employed and the flame should be kept soft and not so rigid as that used for welding.

**Applying
Brazing
Spelter**

The parts to be joined are first fluxed with a liquid or paste borax flux. The work is then brought to a bright red heat and more flux applied. This second fluxing is done automatically if granular spelter mixed with borax powder is used, since the flux and spelter are sprinkled on to the joint together. Alternatively, spelter in rod form is rubbed or wiped round the joint, and in either case the spelter melts and flows into the joint. Should granular spelter refuse to unite in places, it may be induced to do so by removing oxide with an iron poker dipped in flux, or by assisting the flow and union of the spelter by applying a heated spelter wire also dipped in flux.

**Brazing Brass
Flanges to
Copper Pipes**

The type of flanged joint shown in Fig. 9 is made by brazing the brass flange to the copper pipe. The end of the copper tube should be slightly expanded to make a close driving fit to the brass flange. An additional refinement is to dress the tube end over a bevel in the jointing face of the flange as shown at B, whereas at A the tube end simply comes flush with the jointing face.

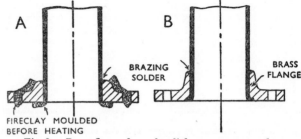

Fig. 9. Brass flanges brazed to light gauge copper tubes.

Before brazing is attempted, fireclay is moulded round the hub of the flange up to the bevelled edge, on the jointing face of the flange and in the bolt-holes (as indicated in Fig. 9), in order to prevent the molten solder overflowing at the top, or running out at the bottom, or running into the bolt-holes. Granular brazing solder and borax powder or solution are then placed in the annular bevelled groove in the hub and the joint is heated in a forge or on a temporary hearth until the solder melts and flows round the bevel and into the joint. The heat should not be too fierce at first, in order to dry out the fireclay evenly. The subsequent heating should be carefully controlled (by dampers or wet rags on the flange if necessary), so that the flange is not heated more rapidly than the tube; too rapid heating of the flange may cause it to expand more quickly than the tube and so spoil the closeness of the fit. The flow and union of the molten granular solder may be assisted with a heated iron poker dipped in flux and the application of a heated solder wire. When all the solder is melted evenly round the flange, the joint should be raised a little from the hearth to allow the solder to set. The joint should then be removed altogether and allowed to cool slowly. Quenching with water is inadvisable, as quick contraction may affect the solder. Finally the tube end is trimmed off flush with the jointing face of the flange.

Making Bronze Welded Joints. For a number of purposes bronze welding is a very satisfactory method of jointing copper pipes, especially those of large diameter, because it allows great flexibility in the arrangement of the joints either on the bench or *in situ*. For example, the branches in heating and sanitation pipework can be joined to a main pipe in any position or at any angle, with swept junctions if required (Fig. 40, p. 92). For one-pipe sanitary installations, batteries of pipes for repeating sets of bathrooms, etc., can be assembled and welded on the bench and because of their comparative lightness and rigidity can easily be transported and hoisted into position on site.

Bronze welded Joints

Fig. 10, A, shows the appearance of a bronze welded straight joint, and B, the method

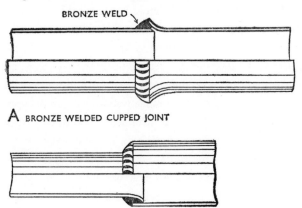

A BRONZE WELDED CUPPED JOINT

B BRONZE WELDED REDUCING JOINT

Fig. 10. *Typical bronze welded joints.*

of reducing from large to small diameter copper tube. Such a method of reduction offers the least resistance to flow, as there is no sharp edge upon which the water can impinge.

With bronze welding the control of the molten metal is much easier than in autogenous welding, since the temperature is considerably lower and, due to the viscosity of molten filler metal and its affinity for copper, the technique of bronze welding allows joints to be made in any position, and even in cramped corners on the job.

Practice with the oxy-acetylene flame is essential and the up-to-date plumber should take advantage of the short courses which are held at institutes and technical schools. Those who already have experience in copper welding should find no difficulty in making bronze welded joints.

Filler Rods

The recent rapid development in bronze welding has been largely due to the establishment by experiment and research, of the correct composition and sizes of bronze and brass filler rods. It has been found, for instance, that the addition of a small amount of phosphorus or silicon to the metal of the rod is of great assistance in preventing oxidation when the joint is made. Phosphor bronze (typical composition 95% copper, 4·5% tin, 0·5% phosphorus) and brass containing about 60% copper, 40% zinc, with small silicon or phosphorus additions, are two alloys widely used as filler rods. For pipe sizes up to $1\frac{1}{2}$ in., a $\frac{1}{16}$ in. diameter rod will be found satisfactory; for pipes 2 in. and upwards, a $\frac{1}{8}$ in. diameter filler rod should be used.

Fluxes for Bronze Welding

Fluxes of the borax type should be used. A paste flux or a powdered flux wetted to make a paste can be more thoroughly and evenly distributed than a flux in powder form. If a powder is used, the rod should be first dipped into water and then into the flux.

Preparation of Bronze Welded Joints

For straight bronze welded joints, the end of one tube is flared out to form a socket by means of a steel drift in the same way as already explained in the section on Compression Joints (p. 23). An angle of 30° for the drift is recommended, and the outside arris of the end of the other tube should be filed off to give a push-tight fit in the socket (see Fig. 10, A). For bronze welding in awkward positions, the joint is more easily made if the socket is not cupped out more than $\frac{1}{8}$ in. from the spigot pipe. If the cup is made much larger, the molten bronze tends to work out of the cup on vertical surfaces such as at the sides of a large horizontal branch joining a vertical pipe, and is more easily manipulated if the cup is small. The parts to be jointed should be thoroughly cleaned.

Further details of the preparation of swept junctions, etc., are given on p. 112 and in the Heating and Sanitation sections of this book (Chapters X and XI).

Oxy-Acetylene Apparatus

As already explained, an oxy-acetylene blowpipe is essential for bronze welding, and care should be taken that the correct size of blowpipe tip is used for a given diameter of pipe and/or gauge of pipe metal. The flame used for bronze welding copper to copper with a phosphor bronze filler rod may be of a "neutral" character, but when using a filler rod containing zinc a slightly oxidising flame reduces to a minimum the volatilisation of the zinc in the filler metal, and the same precaution is essential when bronze welding copper pipes to brass fittings such as traps, stop-taps, unions etc., in order to avoid volatilisation of the zinc in the brasswork. When welding, the tip of the luminous cone of the flame should be kept about $\frac{1}{8}$ in. away from the molten metal of the filler rod.

Procedure for Bronze Welding

When the joint is assembled, either on the bench or *in situ*, proceed as follows:—

The copper pipe in the region of the joint is slightly preheated by the flame, but at no time should the copper be allowed to melt. The main function of the flame is to heat the copper tube jointing surface locally to approximately the same temperature as the

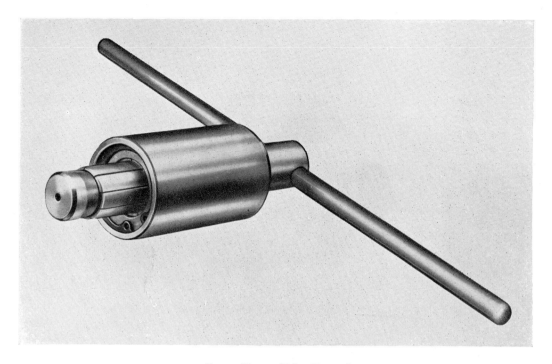

PLATE V.   *Tube Expander.*

(*Used to form capillary socket on tube end. Joints so formed may be made with soft solder or copper - silver - phosphorous or similar brazing alloys.*)

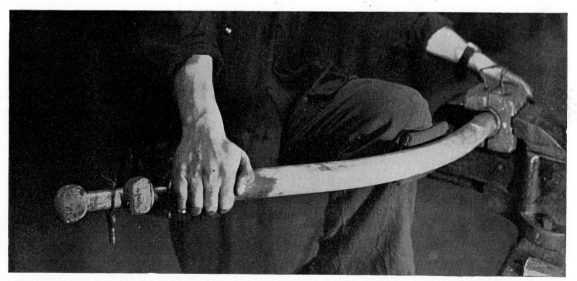

PLATE VI.   *Bending a 1½ in. light gauge tube with spring loading.   (See p. 45.)*

To face page 38.

PLATE VII.   *Filling a tube with lead loading.*   (*See p.* 46.)

melting point of the filler metal, a temperature which is not sufficient to cause fusion of the copper, but which will permit alloying by diffusion, between the filler metal and the copper of the tube.

A spot of filler metal is first melted off the filler rod and deposited in the flared socket. When adhesion has been made at one spot in the socket the filler metal already deposited should be reheated to fluid condition and fresh filler rod added at the edge. This fresh spot should "simmer out" to form an advanced "wet" edge on the copper. This operation is repeated, watching that each spot "simmers out" with a thin wet edge, indicating proper "tinning," as it is often called. To work otherwise would probably result in the bronze flooding over the joint and would simply make an edge adhesion with very little strength and possible leakage of the finished joint. This detail applies equally when bronze welding to brasswork. This process is continued round the socket until the joint is completed. In order to keep control over the filler metal, it is important that each spot of filler metal should be deposited upon the metal already in the joint and not in front of it.

In an attempt to simplify the preparation of bronze welded joints, especially for awkward junctions, there has been placed upon the market a range of copper and copper alloy jointing fittings known as "weldable fittings," illustrations of which are shown on p. 106, Fig. 45.

Weldable Fittings

Making a Copper Welded Joint. Autogenous copper welding is employed for jointing tubes where it is important that the metal of the joint and tube should be of approximately the same colour and composition. This is the case with tubes conveying corrosive liquids in certain chemical plant, where the conjunction of dissimilar metals might give rise to corrosion. In building work, the question of resistance to corrosive acids does not generally arise and autogenous welding is used only where appearance is important. For instance, copper welding may be employed for the joints in the tubes of a buried heating panel, or if it is intended to expose the service pipes to, and the waste-pipes from, a range of lavatory basins, copper welding allows the joints to be buffed down so that they are invisible. The whole battery of pipes can then be polished, lacquered or plated to present a very neat finish. The same remarks apply to copper tubular furniture. (Sometimes, however, the brass-coloured streak at a bronze welded or brazed joint is concealed by rubbing with copper sulphate ("blue stone") to give a thin film of copper. This, of course, is not a very durable expedient.)

Autogenous Welding

It was not until comparatively recently that ordinary copper could be welded "autogenously," that is to say, by direct fusion with or without a copper filler rod. One of the difficulties to be overcome was that ordinary copper contains about 0·03% oxygen, which tends to react with the reducing gases of the flame to form steam bubbles, giving porosity near the weld. However, the filler rods for this process nearly always contain a deoxidising agent and are thus deoxidising in character, and a good welder, by skilful application of the rod, can make satisfactory welds under a borax flux in ordinary "tough pitch"—that is oxygen-bearing—copper. It is, however, much more satisfactory to use

Tough Pitch and Deoxidised Copper

deoxidised copper—that is, copper from which the oxygen has been removed—for parts that are to be fabricated by welding; and all the copper tubes now supplied for building purposes are deoxidised. In addition, filler rods usually contain a small percentage of silver to increase their fluidity.

Filler Rods and Flux

Although it is claimed that autogenous welding can be carried out with deoxidised materials without a flux, it is generally advisable to use a flux of the borax type for the protection of the copper, which readily becomes oxidised and absorbs gases at welding heat.

Welding Flame

The welding flame should be "neutral" and the point of the luminous cone should be kept about $\frac{1}{8}$ in. from the metal and at right angles to it, so that the enveloping part of the flame will protect the copper from the oxidising effect of the air.

Straight Joints

Joints in tubes can be made by butting the two ends and fusing them together with the addition of metal from a filler rod, or by forming flanges upon the tube ends and fusing the metal of the outwardly-turned flanges, which provide sufficient reinforcement without the use of a filler rod (Fig. 11). The amount of metal turned out to form the

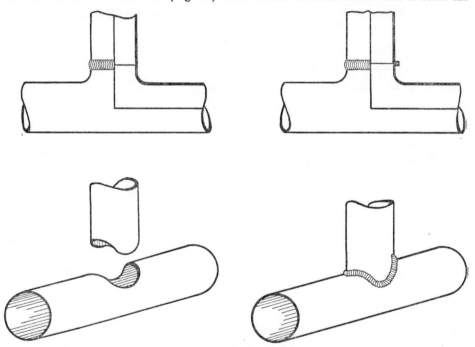

Fig. 11. *Autogenous or copper welded joints.*

flanges should be from $\frac{1}{16}$ in. to $\frac{1}{8}$ in. according to the diameter and thickness of the pipe. One authority recommends that the projection of the flanges measured from the outside of the pipe should be approximately one and a half times the thickness of the metal, and not more. The flanges should be given square shoulders and should butt closely together in order to avoid any cavity when welding takes place. For joining vertical pipes by welding, it is better to flange the top pipe only. A very square shoulder should be formed and the spigot end filed level to fit closely on to the shoulder. If this point is not closely observed holes may occur when welding, and will have to be made up with a filler rod. A flared socket joint as in bronze welding is also sometimes used with a copper filler rod.

Branch joints may be formed by

Branch Joints

(1) Cutting a hole in the main pipe and working out the edges of the hole to form a tee to which the branch is butted and the joint welded by building up a fillet round the joint with a copper filler rod (Fig. 11).

(2) Forming a cupped socket on the tee and building up the filler metal round the socket in the same way as in bronze welding.

(3) Cutting a hole in the main pipe of the same diameter as the bore of the branch pipe, shaping the end of the branch pipe to fit snugly on the outside of the main pipe and welding round the junction with a filler rod (Fig. 11).

For branches entering a main pipe at an angle, method (3) probably requires less skill in the preparation of the pipes, and while it may be suitable for water service pipes and heating installations, for sanitation pipes one of the other methods, as described in Chapter XI, provides an "easier" swept junction with no risk of the weld obstructing the interior of the pipe.

Owing to the high conductivity of copper the pipes in the neighbourhood of the joint must first be thoroughly preheated. The joint is then "tack" welded in two or three spots to hold the pipes in alignment while the rest of the weld is made. Starting from a "tack" the welding proceeds round the pipe by the local fusion of the pipe ends with the filler rod or by the fusing down of the flanges. At the finish of welding a flanged joint it may be necessary to employ the filler rod to fill a small cavity which sometimes occurs at the starting and finishing point of the weld. Joints made on the bench can, of course, be rotated so that welding takes place only on the top. Welding *in situ* is more difficult, especially at the under side and back of a horizontal pipe which is near a wall. In such cases there will be less risk of burning holes through the weld if the joint is made with a spigot and socket and welded with a filler rod. The finished joints, if properly executed, have a surface of regular "waves," as indicated in Fig. 11, due to the repeated application and removal of the flame as the weld proceeds. The widths of the joints on light gauge tubes need not be more than about $\frac{1}{4}$ in. to $\frac{1}{2}$ in. according to the diameter and gauge of the tubes.

Making a Weld

The copper forming the weld is in the as-cast condition, and in order to improve its homogeneity and crystal structure, and to restore its strength, the weld may be hammered carefully with light blows while still red hot, the blows being increased in force as the metal cools.

Hammering Welds

CHAPTER IV

BENDING COPPER TUBES

One of the chief advantages in the use of copper for all pipework in building is the ease with which copper tubes can be bent. The plumber's or fitter's ability to make a bend easily on the job may save the use of a number of angle fittings, allows a minimum obstruction to the flow of water or gas, and enables the pipes to be carried easily round offsets in walls and floors and other obstructions. Bends may also allow a long length of tube to expand and contract without the danger of high stresses being set up.

Distortion during Bending

For a proper understanding of the various techniques and tools employed in bending, it is desirable that the reader should appreciate clearly what deformations take place in a copper tube when it is bent.

The walls of a straight tube are parallel and must remain parallel after bending if the true round section of the tube is to be maintained in the bend. The original length of the tube, o–o (Fig. 12, A), remains unaltered after bending only along the centre line

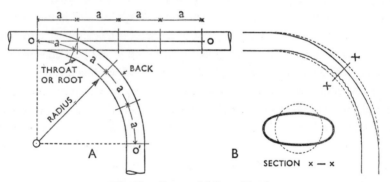

Fig. 12.   *True and deformed bends.*

A. *True bend. Each division* a *represents a "throw" in making the bend (see p. 50).*
B. *Deformation of bend in unsupported tubes.*

of the tube (o–o'), and it follows that the inside or throat of the bend is shortened and compressed and the outside or back is lengthened and stretched. The shortening and lengthening will tend to produce a flattening of the back and an inward kinking of the

Loading for Hand Bending

throat, with a spreading of the sides of the bend (Fig. 12, B). Thus collapse of the tube in the bend will occur unless precautions are taken to prevent it. When bending by manual methods it is, therefore, necessary to support the tube walls while bending takes place. This support can be provided by filling or "loading" the tube and the materials commonly

42

PLATE VIII.   *Introducing the ram of a sand compressor before loading the tube with sand.*
(See p. 50.)

PLATE IX.   *Filling a tube with sand loading.*   (*See pp.* 48 *to* 50.)

used are: (1) steel springs, (2) lead, (3) pitch or resin, or a mixture of pitch and resin, (4) sand. There are also available special low melting point metallic fillers. Bending by machine can be carried out without filling in the smaller pipe sizes, as the special formers or mandrels employed support the sides of the tube (see section of former, Fig. 18, p. 53), and so prevent it from becoming oval in section. Both machine and hand methods of bending are fully described in later sections of this chapter.

Light gauge copper tubes to B.S. 659–1955 are supplied by manufacturers in "half-hard" temper unless otherwise specified, which gives them a desirable degree of rigidity and strength, and minimises damage in transit. This half-hard temper is imparted to the copper by the cold work imposed on the tube in drawing it through a die to its final size during the last stages of manufacture.

Annealing a copper tube to restore it to soft temper consists of heating to dull red **Annealing** heat (as seen in a subdued light), corresponding to about 600° C. Care should be taken not to overheat. The tube may be cooled quickly by plunging it into water while still hot, or it can be left to cool naturally, the method of cooling not affecting in any way the degree of softness obtained. Plate IV (facing p. 29), shows the process of annealing a copper tube within the length of the bend (indicated by the chalk-marks) by means of a powerful blowlamp. The length of the bend is measured from a rough full-size drawing (made in chalk on a cement floor or on a piece of sheet iron if the bend is to be made at red heat), upon which the pipe can be laid for checking as bending proceeds.

If a small-diameter copper tube is given a slight bend or offset by simple manual methods without loading, it will generally be found that a tube of half-hard temper tends to collapse less than soft or annealed tube. However, if a tube is to be bent cold when loaded, or by machine, it will generally be found that the work is made considerably easier if the tube is first annealed on the length containing the bend. Cold work imposed on the tube by bending has the effect of hardening it but will not restore it completely to its original half-hard temper.

Tubing with thick walls has less tendency to collapse when bent than thin-walled tubing of the same diameter.

Heavy copper tubes (as in Tables I and II, pp. 16, 17) can be forge-bent while red **Bending** hot in a similar manner to that employed in bending mild steel and wrought iron barrel. **Thick-walled** They can also be bent with advantage by the sundry machines on the market, if provided **Tube** with proper formers, and by some of the other bending methods described below for light gauge tubing. When using handpull machines for heavy gauge tubes, it is always advisable to anneal the section to be bent and so save labour and undue stress on the machine.

There is no difficulty in bending light gauge tubes if ordinary skill is used. Bends **Bending Light** can be easily and quickly made with a little practice, especially if the modest outlay for **Gauge Tubes** a bending machine for the smaller sizes is incurred. The bending of light gauge tubes by hand methods, however, may often be required, particularly by those who only

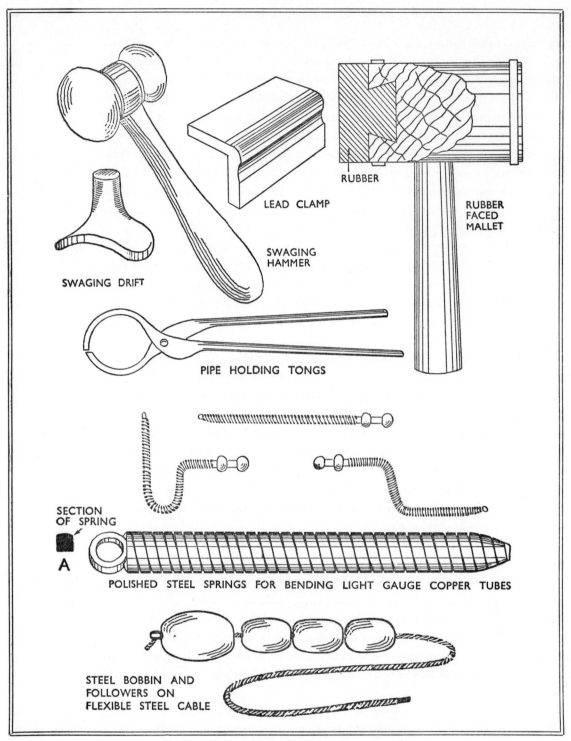

RUBBER

LEAD CLAMP

SWAGING
HAMMER

RUBBER
FACED
MALLET

SWAGING DRIFT

PIPE HOLDING TONGS

SECTION
OF SPRING

A

POLISHED STEEL SPRINGS FOR BENDING LIGHT GAUGE COPPER TUBES

STEEL BOBBIN AND
FOLLOWERS ON
FLEXIBLE STEEL CABLE

Fig. 13. Tools used in bending light gauge copper tubes.

occasionally have to make bends, especially in the larger sizes of tube, for which machines are expensive. These methods of bending when using the various loading materials are described below.

Flexible spiral steel springs of the type shown in Fig. 13 may be used as a loading to support the tube walls while the bend is made. It is generally considered that the best section for the spring is that shown at A in Fig. 13. These springs have wooden handles which may be unscrewed and replaced with an eyelet into which is hooked an extension rod, so that the spring may be inserted and withdrawn when a bend is made in the middle of a length of tube. **Steel Springs**

Springs are obtainable for bending tubes in all the standard sizes from $\frac{1}{2}$ in. up to 2 in. diameter, which is the maximum size for spring loading. Only easy bends should be attempted with spring loading, and the minimum radii to the throat are approximately 3 diameters for tubes up to 1 in. and 4 diameters for $1\frac{1}{4}$ in. to 2 in. tubes.

Making Bends with Spring Loading. The following are points especially to be borne in mind when making bends by hand:—

(1) 1 in. diameter tubes can be bent without annealing, but in larger sizes the length of tube in the bend should be first thoroughly annealed. It is better to anneal too long a length than too short, for if the first annealing is insufficient, it may be impossible to complete the bend in one operation, or, if the bend is nearly completed, to insert the spring after a second annealing has been carried out. For this reason, when making a 90° bend in the $1\frac{1}{4}$ in. to 2 in. sizes of tube, it is advisable first to make a slow bend to about 45°, to withdraw the spring, and to re-anneal the length of the bend. It should then be possible to reinsert the spring and to complete the bend.

(2) The tube should be slightly over-bent by a few degrees and then pulled back to the required angle. The effect of this is to pull out the throat which, in bending, is pressed in against the spring, and to pull in the sides of the tube, which in bending, have a tendency to spread out, and thereby to restore the true section of the tube and to release any pressure on the spring.

(3) To withdraw the spring easily its diameter should be reduced by inserting a tommy bar in the end loop and twisting it in the direction in which it is wound at the same time as it is pulled out. Slightly greasing the spring will aid withdrawal.

(4) The use of tools such as a dresser should be avoided when using a spring loading, since any over-working, besides unnecessarily hardening the copper, may imprison the spring, which may be damaged when it is withdrawn. A rubber-faced mallet (Fig. 13) may, however, be used to take an offset out of "twist" if the two bends forming the offset have inadvertently been made out of line. This use of the mallet applies, of course, to double bends made with any loading. Plate VI (facing p. 38) shows a $1\frac{1}{2}$ in. light gauge tube being bent with a steel spring loading. Note the special lead blocks in the vice. These are not essential, but for all forms of hand bending they hold the tube very firmly without a tendency to crush it.

Making Bends with Lead Loading. Owing to the power required and the difficulty of melting out the lead, it is not economical to make bends with lead loading in tubes of greater diameter than $1\frac{1}{2}$ inch. For smaller tubes it is, however, a safe and efficient loading. Sharp bends can be made successfully with radii as small as 2 diameters for tubes up to 1 in. and $2\frac{1}{2}$ diameters for $1\frac{1}{4}$ in. and $1\frac{1}{2}$ in. tubes.

Bending Lead-loaded tubes

The length of tube to form the bend should first be thoroughly annealed. It is better to anneal too much than not enough, as to re-anneal entails loading and reloading.

A wooden plug should be inserted into one end of the tube and lead poured into the other end to a height well above the proposed bend. Plate VII (facing p. 39) illustrates this operation. Only soft lead, such as melted sheet lead scrap, free from solder inclusions, should be used. The copper tube should be securely fixed or held with tongs, since it becomes very hot when the lead is poured in, and great care should be taken that the tube is thoroughly dry, especially if it has been quenched after annealing. If the tube is at all damp, steam will be formed and will blow out the lead, with grave risk to the operator. It is therefore advisable to warm the tube well before pouring the lead. The pouring should be continuous in order to avoid the formation of air pockets or "cold shuts," which might cause the tube to collapse when the bend is made.

When the bend is finished any slight corrugations in the throat, which will project outwards if the tube has been properly loaded, should be dressed back with a boxwood tool such as that shown in Fig. 14, p. 47. If the corrugations are pronounced, as they may be in sharp bends, a steel swaging hammer, shown in Fig. 13, may have to be used. The use of this tool should, however, be avoided whenever possible, because marks are left on the tube unless the work is in very expert hands. A special set of polished steel swaging drifts (Fig. 13) is used by coppersmiths to obtain highly finished bends.

The lead has then to be melted out, for which two powerful blowlamps or blowpipes are an advantage, and when a large number of bends have to be made in a workshop, this may be conveniently done by dropping the bends into the tank of molten lead which is being used for loading. Care must, of course, be taken to see that all the lead is removed from the bore of the tube.

Loading with Low Melting Point Alloys

Instead of lead for loading, a very low melting-point metallic composition can be employed, which can be maintained in its molten state at temperatures lower than the boiling point of water. The procedure with such fillers is to plug one end of the tube and load with the compounds in their molten state. They solidify quickly and the tube can be bent to the required shape and then the filler removed by dipping the whole into a tank of boiling water, when the filler will run out and leave the interior of the tube perfectly clean. Hot bending of tubes cannot, of course, be carried out with this type of loading, as the alloy is molten at temperatures such as would be used for such bending.

Making Bends with Pitch and Resin Loading. The following procedure may be applied when loadings of pitch and resin or a mixture of pitch and resin are used. Bending with any of these loadings is easier than with lead loading, and is to be preferred for

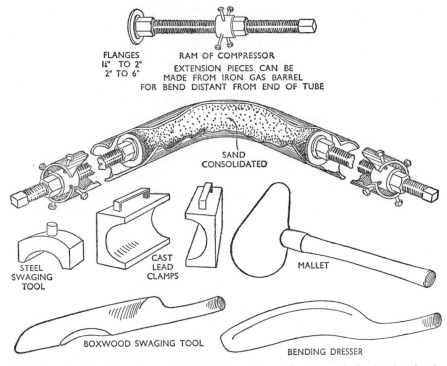

FLANGES
1¼" TO 2"
2" TO 6"

RAM OF COMPRESSOR
EXTENSION PIECES CAN BE
MADE FROM IRON GAS BARREL
FOR BEND DISTANT FROM END OF TUBE

SAND
CONSOLIDATED

STEEL
SWAGING
TOOL

CAST
LEAD
CLAMPS

MALLET

BOXWOOD SWAGING TOOL

BENDING DRESSER

Fig. 14.   Special sand compressor for hot bending with sand loading, and other incidental tools.

tubes over 1½ in. in diameter because less force is required, the loaded tube is lighter to handle, and loading and unloading are easier. Tubes up to 6 in. or more in diameter can be bent with these loadings. The minimum radii to the throat for bends made with pitch or resin loadings are usually about 2 diameters for 1¼ in. and 1½ in. tubes and 4 diameters for 2 in. to 4 in. tubes.

First anneal the length of tube within the range of the proposed bend or bends. Attempts should never be made to anneal a tube already loaded with pitch or resin, as to do so will probably cause a dangerous explosion. The pitch or resin must be slowly heated until it is liquid, taking care it does not catch fire. If this accident should occur it is best to smother the mouth of the vessel containing the pitch with a wet sack, and one should be kept ready soaked in case of such an accident. The tube is plugged at one end with a wooden plug and heated to a temperature at which it can be comfortably held with a piece of sacking. The loading is then poured in at the top end, first making sure that the tube is properly secured, as the filling will take an hour or two to solidify. The loading shrinks as it cools and it may be necessary to add further loading for the first few minutes. If any resin runs down on the outside of the tube it should be left till it is quite cold, when it will shell off easily. To attempt to scrape it off when hot will only spread it into a sticky mess over a larger area.

When the loading is cold and solid, and not before, bends can be pulled in the manner described for bending with lead loading, or they can, of course, be made in a machine in cases where the thinness of gauge or sharpness of bend, or both, requires such loading. In special cases proper bending blocks, and a hydraulic press for the power, may be employed, but this is usually beyond the province of the average plumbing firm.

After bending, the tube is heated and the loading run out. Care must be taken to see that the interior is free from pitch, or from carbon formed during the reheating.

Removing Dents from Bends

Sometimes a bend may be badly dented or crimped, or a finished bend may be damaged in transit or by misadventure on the job. In Fig. 13 a steel bobbin and followers are shown which may be used to rectify any such damage. For instance, if a bend is dented, it is heated up on the dent with the flame of a blowlamp, or the flame of a welding torch, to soften that part locally. The polished steel bobbin, well greased, is then driven in at the nearest end with a piece of iron barrel and heavy hammer. By threading followers on one by one, the bobbin is then driven past the dent and pulled back by means of cable. Ordinary malleable iron "followers" as used in bending lead pipes are sufficient, but the bobbin must be a good fit and not too tight. Care must be taken not to damage the tube with the end of the iron barrel. Alternatively, with large-diameter tube the dent can be driven out with a "dummy" or bumping bar. This is best done with the dent at red heat, as the stroke and force of the blows made with the dummy are limited by the diameter of the tube.

Cold Bending with Sand Loading

Making Bends with Sand Loading. Sand loading consists of filling the tube with dry sand well rammed to consolidate it. Easy open bends may be made cold in tube not exceeding 2 in. in diameter by placing the loaded tube between the lead-covered jaws of a vice and lifting slowly upwards. The throat of the bend should be carefully watched and if crimps begin to form, the tube should be unloaded and softened and the crimps removed by means of a polished steel bobbin driven in by a piece of gas barrel on the followers and by carefully swaging with a round-faced swaging hammer.

Hot Bending

Sand-loaded tubes can of course be bent in a machine or in formers of various kinds. With sand loading, bending with the tube at red heat is generally the better method and is essential for sharp bends or bends in tubes having a greater diameter than 2 inches. Bends can be made hot in tubes having diameters up to 6 in., and at radii as small as $2\frac{1}{2}$ diameters for 1 in to 2 in. tubes and 4 diameters for $2\frac{1}{2}$ in. to 4 in. tubes present no difficulty. The procedure for hot bending is as follows:—

(1) Plug the lower end of the tube with a tight-fitting wooden plug. If sharp or intricate bends are required the plug should be secured against drawing out by drilling the side and inserting a screw, as the act of bending will exert a certain amount of "hydraulic" pressure on the plugs. After bending, the screw hole will have to be filled or the tube end cut off above the hole.

(2) Fill the tube with hot dry sand through a funnel, consolidating it by tamping continuously on the floor and dressing the outside with a piece of dry deal or other soft timber. Ramming with a tommy bar is useful, but the constant tamping and dressing

are the most effective. This procedure is shown in Plate VIII. It is important that the sand should be absolutely dry, as any moisture in the sand may generate steam when the tube is heated, and this may cause an explosion. The sand can be conveniently dried on a red-hot iron plate.

(3) When the sand is solid and within $1\frac{1}{2}$ in. of the top of the tube, drive a tight-fitting, slow-taper plug in the end. The tube is now ready for bending.

(4) A drawing of the required bend should be made and a bent wire template prepared.

(5) Bring the section of pipe to be contained in the bend to red heat with a suitable flame or in the forge. If the latter, only a slow draught should be used and the pipe watched closely and rotated in the fire to get an even red temperature. The expansion by heat may have loosened the sand, so the pipe should be quickly turned on end and gently retamped, and the top plug driven in to take up any slackness. If done quickly, the pipe will still be at red heat, and the bend may be started by dumping it heavily on the floor, adding the weight of the arms. This action is illustrated in Fig. 15. This method helps to keep the sand solid in the bottom end of the tube and to counteract any looseness which may occur from stretching of the outside wall of the bend.

(6) Redrive the top plug and reheat.

(7) Place the tube in the lead-clamped jaws of the vice and finish the bend to the required sweep and angle by judicious heating and pulling. The bent wire template taken from the drawing of the bend is useful to check the shape of the bend and can be held on the tube while bending is taking place. Irregular bending is usually caused by uneven heating, as the tube will bend where it is hottest. If the bend tends to vary from the template it may be necessary to repeat the section already bent before proceeding with the rest of the bend.

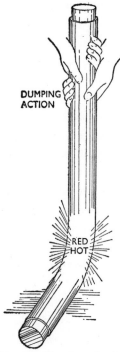

Fig. 15. *Starting a bend in a sand loaded tube.*

(8) When the bend is complete it is lightly swaged to produce a smooth finish and to restore the walls to their original temper. The tube is then unloaded and cleaned up.

Use of Sand Compressor

With sand loading as just described there is always a risk that the sand is not packed sufficiently tightly or that it becomes loose after heating and bending have begun. This difficulty is overcome by the use of a special sand compressor which is illustrated in Fig. 14 and can be seen in Plates VIII and IX. This tool is provided with ram plates

D

to fit tubes having diameters from $1\frac{1}{4}$ in. to 6 in. The threads on the rams are standard gas threads, so that if a bend is required in the middle of a long length of pipe, extensions can be made to the rams with iron barrel, as will be seen from the illustrations already referred to. It will be realised that this compressor can quite easily be made up.

To take the thrust of the screwed plunger, two holes should be drilled in small tubes and four in large tubes. Sufficient length should be left in the tube to allow the holed ends to be cut off after the bend is completed.

The compressor is introduced into one end of the tube and fixed in position. The ram should be a close fit to prevent the sand escaping. If it is a loose fit a little soap smeared on the edges prevents fine sand from escaping.

Plate VIII (facing p. 42) shows the compressor being introduced into one end of the tube to be bent. The two centre chalk-lines shown indicate the length of tube contained in the proposed bend. The outside marks indicate the positions in which the ram faces are fixed. The less the amount of sand, the more solid it can be made in the section containing the bend. From 4 in. to 5 in. of sand beyond the section containing the bend is sufficient to make the bend. This is shown diagrammatically in Fig. 14.

The tube is then up-ended as shown in Plate IX (facing p. 43) and filled with well-burnt silver sand. A funnel is used to fill the tube. At the same time, the sides of the tube are struck continuously, as indicated in the photograph, to help consolidate the sand. This process is continued for about five minutes and the sand packed up to the top line.

The other ram is then introduced and fixed in the top end. The tube is placed in the clamp of the vice and the two rams tightened up with the spanner provided, or with a short tommy bar for the larger sizes. Heat is then applied to the loaded section and the rams again screwed up to take up the space caused by expansion. A few blows with a piece of deal on the sides will help. By this means the sand is packed almost stone-hard and the tube, when brought to red heat, is ready for bending.

Bending with Sand Compressor

The bend is pulled in a series of "throws," making the first throw adjoining the chalk-line nearest the vice. Plate X (opposite) shows the first throw being made. The flame is then held away for a moment to see if there are any slight puckers, which, if the sand is tight, will project outwards. Heat is again applied, the ram tightened, the bend pulled slightly open, the ram tightened again, and the throat dressed smooth with the boxwood swaging dresser and mallet or with an old bending dresser. When the bend is reheated in preparation for the next throw, the centre of heat should be about $1\frac{1}{2}$ in. away from the centre of the first heat. The compressor should be tightened up after every heating and dressing, as otherwise the sand becomes loose. A right-angled bend is completed in three or four throws, the heating being practically continuous except when the dresser is applied. Pulling should not be done unless the tube is at red heat all round, as otherwise there is risk of breaking the back. The dressing in the throat thickens the copper so that by this method the back of the bend is not unduly stretched.

LEAD CLAMPS

COMPRESSOR

PLATE X. *Pulling the first "throw" in a sand-loaded tube. (See p. 50.)*

PLATE XI.   *Bending a light gauge copper tube in a machine.*   (*See p. 52.*)

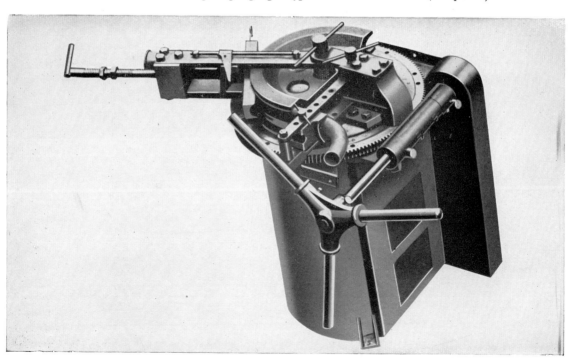

PLATE XII,   *A ratchet or geared bending machine.*   (*See p. 52.*)

If all the copper wall surfaces are at red heat, it is quite easy to pull the pipe round for each throw. A piece of deal quartering may be bound on to the tube to assist leverage when bending short ends.

A gas blowpipe with air blast is being used in the photographs, but an oxy-acetylene blowpipe with a multiple jet provides an excellent means of heating. Alternatively a powerful blowlamp can be used, placing asbestos sheet behind to concentrate the heat on the required part of the tube.

The bend should be pulled a few degrees beyond the required angle and then, after heating, pulled back. This rectifies any slight depression of the throat and spreading of the sides of the bend which may have occurred, i.e. it pulls the throat out and contracts the sides, bringing the tube back to true section. If a second bend is required only one compressor need be removed, the extra sand added, and the compressor refixed.

Simple Hand Bending Device

One of the simplest devices for hand bending small-diameter tubes is made by boring holes equal in diameter to the outer diameter of the tubes in a wood block or plank 3 in. to 4 in. thick and then, by means of a gouge, forming easy bend channels in the thickness of the block. The tube to be bent is placed through the suitable hole and bent downwards in the channel, "humouring" it along according to the sharpness of the bend required. Only easy bends on loaded tube should be attempted by this means.

Another simple device is indicated in Fig. 16. It consists of a former and an eyelet to hold the tube down. The tube is pressed down in the former, which is bolted on to a bench or plank. A home-made type can be cast in old unusable solder or other "hards," or made in hardwood. An eyelet should be used that is large enough to allow a protecting sleeve of lead or other metal to be inserted between the copper and the comparatively sharp ring of the eye. Tubes up to $1\frac{1}{2}$ in. diameter may be bent by this means.

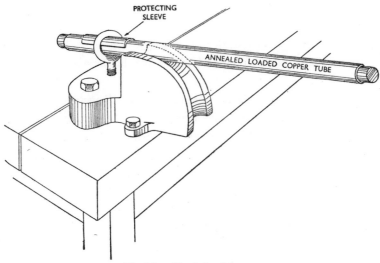

PROTECTING SLEEVE

ANNEALED LOADED COPPER TUBE

Fig. 16. *Simple bend former.*

Bending by Machine. The purchase of a bending machine will prove economical where a number of bends are required in the smaller sizes of tubes (see Plate XI, p. 51).

Machines of various types and sizes, worked by direct hand power, are constructed to bend copper tubes up to 2 in. diameter, and are small and light enough to be transported to the job. For diameters greater than this, ratchet action or geared machines should be used, such as that illustrated in Plate XII (facing p. 51). Such machines, however, are expensive and for firms only occasionally doing large size pipework one of the hand bending methods should be satisfactory. Alternatively, compression, soldered or weldable copper or copper-alloy bend fittings can be used, but the cost generally exceeds that of a hand-made bend using the appropriate methods previously described and illustrated.

Some bending machines on the market are so small and compact that they are practically hand tools. Fig. 17 illustrates a small tool for bending $\frac{1}{4}$ in., $\frac{3}{8}$ in. and $\frac{1}{2}$ in. tube, unloaded. It can be carried in the kit and bends can, if necessary, be made on a fixed pipe. The illustration shows the method of operation.

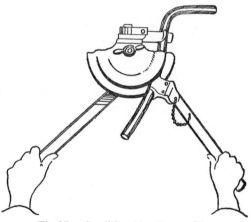

Fig. 17.   *Small hand bending machine.*

There are a number of machines on the market of admirable design such as the "Hilmor," the "Kennedy," the "Scols," and the "Tubela," etc., all capable of producing satisfactory bends in light gauge tube, loaded or unloaded, according to lightness or otherwise of gauge or to the sharpness of bend required. They are designed to be practically fool-proof, and bends can be made to the requirements with a high degree of certainty. Right- or left-hand bends, or bends of intricate shape, can be produced within the limitations of the radii of the quadrant formers.

The fact that bends can be made in tubes up to $2\frac{1}{2}$ in. diameter and in the majority of gauges, without loading the tube, means a large saving of time to the plumber or fitter, and is accounted for by the design of the machines, which allows the wall of the tube to be properly supported against collapsing while bending takes place. In all cases the tube is bent round a quadrant former, the edge of which has a semi-circular groove into which the tube fits tightly, so that the throat and sides of the bend are firmly supported.

In the types of machine most generally used, the tube is bent by means of pressure applied to a back guide. The guide is a hollowed piece of steel which is placed on the back of the copper tube to protect it, and an adjustable roller is pressed upon the guide at a point, the exact position of which enables the bend to be made without ripples occurring in the throat and without over-compression and thickening of the throat metal which would reduce the bore of the tube.

It follows that for the tube to be properly supported, the former and back guide must be of exact size to suit the outside diameter of the tube. The machines are therefore designed to take formers and guides for each diameter of tube within their respective ranges.

Standard formers are usually swept to make bends the radius of which is equal to three diameters of the tube to be bent. Formers of sharper radii than the standard indicated can be obtained, but to use a smaller radius entails loading the tube if good clear-bore bends are to be obtained. Alternatively a draw-bar machine, as described later in this section, may be used.

In the past, makers of bending machines recommended that bends on half-hard copper should not be attempted without annealing. It is, however, not now considered necessary to follow this procedure in the case of tubes up to and including 1 inch. Above this size it is advisable to soften the part of the tube to be bent, otherwise perfect bends will not be obtained and undue stresses will be put on the machine. It is often found that when a bend is made without first annealing the tube there is a small bump at each end of the bend. Where annealing has been carried out these bumps will not appear.

Annealing for Machine Bending

It has been explained how the throat and sides of the bend in an unloaded tube are supported against collapsing. Corrugations will, however, occur in the throat of a bend if the pressure of the roller upon the back guide is exerted in the wrong place. The correct pressure point is a certain distance in front of the bending point, which is where

Distortion of Tube in Machine-made Bends

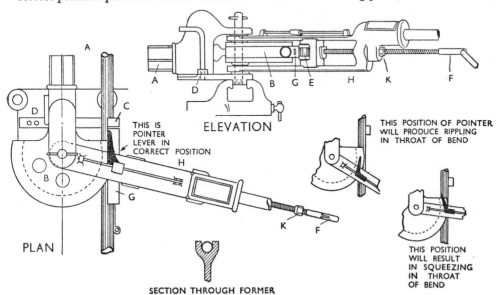

Fig. 18. *Details of a "Hilmor" bending machine: A. Lug for gripping machine in pipe vice, B. Former, C. Stop, D. Stop bar, E. Roller, F. Spindle for adjusting roller, G. Back guide, H. Lever, K. Lock nut.*

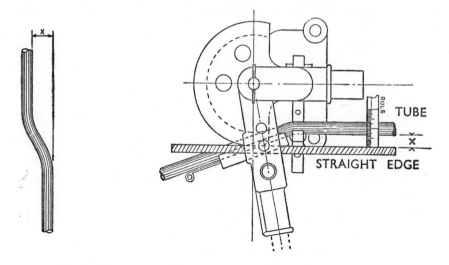

First bend tube to required bevel and set in machine as shown. Place straight-edge against outside edge of former and parallel with tube. When set to given dimension, x, bend in the usual way.

Fig. 19.   To make an offset or double bend.

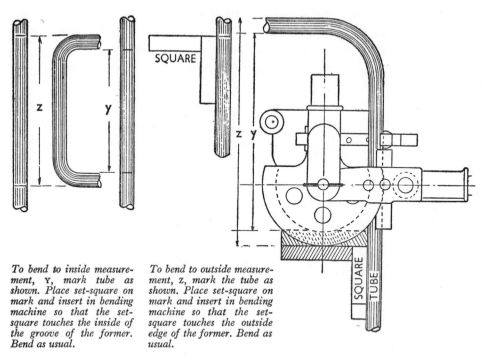

To bend to inside measurement, Y, mark tube as shown. Place set-square on mark and insert in bending machine so that the set-square touches the inside of the groove of the former. Bend as usual.

To bend to outside measurement, z, mark the tube as shown. Place set-square on mark and insert in bending machine so that the set-square touches the outside edge of the former. Bend as usual.

Fig. 20.   To make double bends.

the tube touches the former before bending takes place. These two points, of course, move forward the same distance apart as the bend is made. If the pressure point is advanced too far in front of the bending point, corrugations will occur. It is important, therefore, that when using a machine the operator does not help the bend round by pushing with his left hand on the free end of the tube. Note that in Plate XI (facing p. 51) the operator has both hands on the machine lever. To apply extra pressure to the tube would advance the pressure point and cause corrugations in the throat. Alternatively the pressure point must not be too close to the bending point, or the metal of the throat will be over-compressed and thickened to reduce the bore of the tube.

Double Bends

Fig. 18 shows the plan and elevation of a "Hilmor" machine. Each gauge and tube diameter requires a quadrant former and a back guide. The machine is fitted with a device which, by proper adjustment, determines automatically the exact point at which the pressure is best applied to the tube. This device is the "pointer" shown in Fig. 18, and too much importance cannot be laid on the proper adjustment of this unit, i.e. it must be parallel with the pipe when the roller is making tight contact with the back of the "guide." Plate XI (facing p. 51) also shows this machine. Care must be taken that the rod on which the pointer is fixed does not become bent. Unsatisfactory bends have been known to be produced without any apparent reason until it was found that this rod had become slightly bent, so causing the pointer to give an incorrect pressure point.

Fig. 19 shows the method of making an offset or double bend. After making the first bend, care must be taken to arrange for the second so that both bends are in the same horizontal plane, or the finished offset will be what is known as "out of winding," or twisted. The necessary instructions are given in the diagram.

Fig. 20 shows how to set up for making a double bend, measurements being taken from outside to outside, or alternatively inside to inside, of the bend. Pains must be taken to set up properly in the machine, as bends incorrectly made cannot be altered afterwards, and carelessness in this respect may mean spoiling the length of tube.

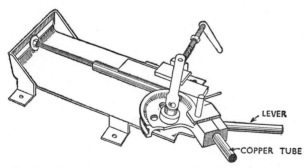

LEVER

COPPER TUBE

Fig. 21. Draw-bar bending machine with stationary mandrel.

Draw-Bar Machines

Fig. 21 shows a form of hand-operated machine designed to produce very true sharp bends on a radius of one and a half times the diameter of tube to the root. This particular machine only bends tubes up to $\frac{7}{8}$ in. in diameter, but a larger machine mounted on a steel bench is obtainable and will bend tubes up to $1\frac{1}{2}$ in. in diameter. These machines are known as draw bar machines, as they incorporate a draw-bar or mandrel which is inserted into the tube and supports the tube up to and at the bending point. True and smoothly finished small-radius bends can be produced by this means.

Fig. 22 shows another type of machine in which an adjustable mandrel, pivoted at its outer end, supports the inside walls of the tube at the bending point and is always

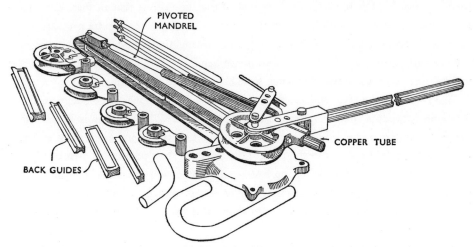

Fig. 22.   Draw-bar bending machine with pivoted mandrel.

tangential to the bend at that point whatever the radius of the former. In these types of machines, as can be seen from the figures, leverage is applied to the former to which the tube is attached, and the former itself revolves while the bend is being made. Draw-bar machines are also made to be power driven, and entirely automatic machines of this type are said to make as many as 200 bends in an hour.

CHAPTER V

COPPER TUBE FITTING

Two of the greatest advantages of light gauge copper tubes are the ease with which they can be installed and their naturally neat appearance. It is important that the first should not form an excuse for slovenly fitting and layout, and that the greatest use should be made of the second by a careful and proper setting out of the work.

Anyone who has examined the plumbing of a large modern building in which copper is employed for the various pipe-lines will appreciate particularly the force of the above remarks in the neat appearance of the numerous pipes carried on the walls or ceilings of these structures.

Where several vertical pipes or drops are grouped together they should be lined up accurately to be parallel and plumb. Where, likewise, service, waste and vent pipes are run horizontally together, they should be kept equidistant as far as possible. The use of the appropriate fittings and bends makes this an easy matter.

Where pipes change direction through 90°, or are offset to pass some break or obstruction in the building, it is generally better to use purpose-made bends rather than sharp cast bends or elbows, in order to impede the free flow of water as little as possible, particularly in hot water and heating installations. Sharp bends are, of course, to be entirely avoided in sanitation pipes, except those which act only as air vents and carry no liquids.

Where several pipes are running in either a vertical or horizontal direction, they should be kept close together but allowing sufficient clearance for fittings to be tightened, and for the screwing of fixing clips. By this means the finished job will present a neat and craftsmanlike appearance.

Setting Out Bends

In setting out bends or offsets it is always worth while to make a full-size drawing on the bench, or if available, on a piece of sheet iron. It is then a simple matter to mark the necessary bending points on the straight pipes and by using the methods described in the previous chapter to obtain the correct angles easily and quickly on the bending machine. In certain cases where several pipes running together change direction, it may be required to keep them equidistant throughout

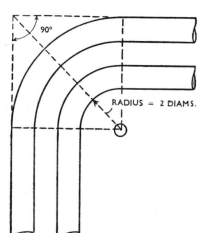

Fig. 23. Setting out of right-angle bends.

RADIUS = 2 DIAMS.

90°

their entire length. Under such conditions only one should be bent on the machine; the other bends, since they will be of different radii, should be made by loading. Figs. 23 and 24 show the setting out of 90° bends and 135° offsets. To set out the work the inner bend is struck first, the angle being checked with a square or protractor. The second bend is then drawn in, allowing sufficient distance between for clipping, etc. The inner bends in the figure are struck on a radius equal to two diameters to the root, or two and a half to the centre for a 90° bend. The bends are struck from the point marked with a small circle on the line bisecting the angle. For the offset the inner bends are made on a radius equal to one diameter to the root or one and a half to the centre of the pipe.

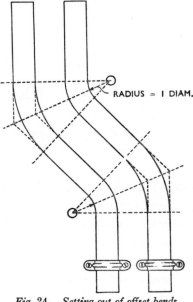

RADIUS = I DIAM.

Fig. 24.   Setting out of offset bends.

Offsets in Sloping Pipes

Where an offset is to be formed in a pipe run having a rise or fall, the projection of the offset may be of such a length that the levels must be maintained, e.g. on a primary flow or return circuit. For example, in the case of a sloping pipe passing round an external corner, the simplest method is to mark the fall on the wall faces on either side of the corner and with chalk draw a connecting line along the brick return (see Fig. 25). The angle of the bend will, of course, be greater than a right angle. The angle may be found graphically as follows:— The angle of the bend is given by the triangle A B C seen in the three-dimensional sketch, Fig. 25a. To draw this triangle accurately on

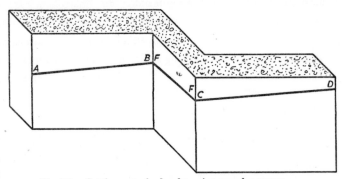

Fig. 25.   Setting out of a bend passing round a corner.

the floor, or on paper, set up the elevations 1 and 2 of the pipe on either side of the corner. Draw the plan of the corner and mark the points A and C on the plan by setting off their horizontal distance, X, from the corner. Project the elevation 3 above, and locate the points A, B and C upon this elevation from the plan and the elevations 1 and 2. In elevation 3 the length of the line A C is the true length of the line A C in the sketch, and the true angle of the pipe can be found by transferring the length of A C in elevation 3 to the line A C on plan produced to A_1 and C_1. The angle, A_1 B C_1 on plan is then the

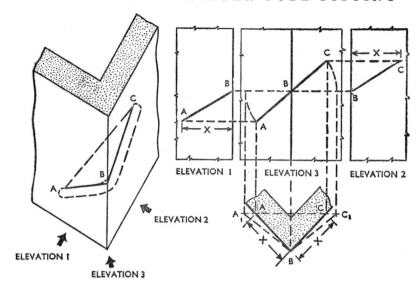

ELEVATION 1

ELEVATION 2

ELEVATION 3

ELEVATION 1

ELEVATION 3

ELEVATION 2

Fig. 25a. Setting out of a bend passing round a corner.

required angle for the bend in the pipe. If the pipe is bent to this angle and is fixed close to the wall, the brickwork at the corner will have to be cut away to accommodate the bend.

Pipe Clips

Copper and brass fixing clips for use with light gauge copper tubes are made in a variety of patterns, some of which are illustrated in Fig. 26. British Standard 1394–1948 covers the design and dimensions of these clips. Useful fixing clips can be formed from light gauge copper tube beaten flat and bent to fit round the pipes; the method of screwing is shown in the illustration.

Expansion of Copper Pipes

The coefficient of thermal expansion of copper is $9 \cdot 22 \times 10^{-6}$ per °F., that is to say, a 1 ft. length of copper becomes $(1 + 0 \cdot 00000922T)$ ft. when heated T° F. For example, for a temperature increase of 100° F., there will be an increase of $\frac{1}{8}$ in. in every 10 ft. run of tube. This amount is somewhat greater than that of iron, but considerably less than that of lead. In the general run of heating and hot water installations, the many bends and offsets which occur will accommodate the amount of movement that takes place due to temperature variations. Where, however, long straight pipe runs are encountered suitable provision must be made to take up any expansion and contraction. This can be done by installing a purpose-made expansion joint in the pipe line. There are three main types of expansion joints, see Fig. 27, the horseshoe or loop (A and B), the bellows (D), and the gland type (C).

Expansion Joints

The loop and horseshoe bends are easily formed and fitted to the pipe line by compression, capillary soldered or welded joints. With this type of expansion joint they must be fixed horizontally, so as to avoid forming air locks at the top of the loop and to ensure proper circulation of the water.

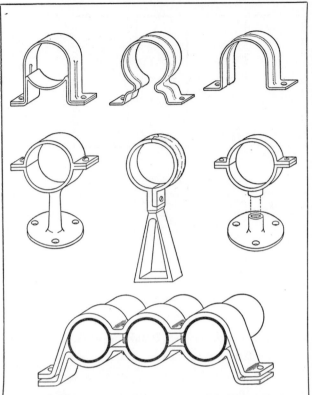

Fig. 26. Some typical copper and brass fixing clips.

The bellows type of expansion joint is obtainable for pipes of 1 in. diameter and upwards, but is more commonly used in large plant. This type of joint is also used in American skyscrapers to take up the expansion in very tall stacks of light gauge copper soil pipes, which, when used on the one-pipe system, are subjected to expansion and contraction caused by the sudden changes of temperature resulting from the alternate discharge of hot and cold water from baths, W.C.s, etc.

Expansion joints of the loop and bellows types are usually of deoxidised non-arsenical copper. Arsenic is omitted since it tends to increase the rate of work-hardening. It is recommended that expansion joints of these types should be annealed annually.

The gland type of joint is made from cast bronze or gunmetal and consists of a free-moving inner sleeve inside an outer casing. The sleeve travels in or out to accommodate pipe movement and is made watertight by a metallic or asbestos packing held in place with a gland nut in the same way as a stuffing box on a tap spindle. The advantage of this type is that it is compact and can be used in any position. Access should be provided for maintenance, such as gland packing or tightening, etc.

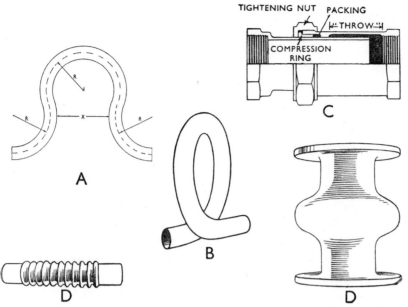

Fig. 27.   *Expansion joints: A, Horseshoe; B, Loop; C, Gland; D, Bellows*

TABLE VIIIa.—*Suitable Radii for Horseshoe Expansion Loops.*

Pipe sizes (ins.)	Radius in inches of bend for expansion (X, Fig. 27, A)							
	1 in.	1½ in.	2 in.	2½ in.	3 in.	4 in.	5 in.	6 in.
¾	15	19	22	25	27	30	34	38
1	16	20	24	27	29	33	38	42
1¼	17	21	26	29	32	36	42	47
1½	18	23	28	31	35	39	46	51
2	20	25	30	34	38	44	51	57
2½	22	27	32	37	42	47	56	62
3	24	30	34	39	45	53	60	67
4	28	34	39	44	48	58	66	75
5	31	39	44	49	54	62	70	78
6	34	42	48	54	59	68	76	83

With sizes to left of zig-zag line expansion loop can be fabricated in one piece. Other sizes require more than 20 ft. of tube for complete loop and must be formed in sections.

CHAPTER VI

PIPE SIZES FOR WATER SERVICES

The general theory in this section is applicable to pipes of any type, and is included in this book, together with useful date for designing the sizes of copper pipes, in the hope that it may be of practical use as a general guide to students, designers and craftsmen.

Mistakes in pipe sizing are too often evident in houses and other types of buildings. For instance, it is sometimes found that when the taps of one or more sanitary fittings are turned on, little or no water can be obtained from others. The remedy for such cases lies in the correct sizes of various pipes, according to their positions in the installation, and since the sizes depend upon the loss of head due to friction, it is desirable that this should be fully understood.

Loss of Head Due to Friction

The loss of head due to friction may be simply explained by an example. In Fig. 28

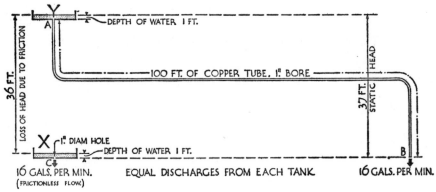

Fig. 28.

are shown two storage tanks in which the water is maintained at a constant depth of 1 ft. The water will flow through a circular hole of 1 in. diameter at C in the bottom of tank *X* at a rate of 16 gallons per minute, assuming that there is no frictional resistance whatever. From tank Y is taken a 1 in. bore copper tube measuring in all 100 ft. from *A* to *B*. To obtain the same rate of discharge at *B* as at *C* it is found that tank *Y* must be raised 36 ft. in order to overcome the friction between the water and the walls of the pipe *AB*. In other words, this 36 ft. of head, or vertical drop, is lost or used up in overcoming friction and is called the loss of head due to friction. The extra 1 ft. of static head in tank *Y*, which is common to both tanks, is necessary to give the same discharge at *B* as at *C*, and is called the velocity head. For the speeds of flow usually encountered in normal pipework in buildings, the velocity head is small, as in the present example, and it is generally accurate enough to take the loss of head due to friction as being equal to the total static head.

The total loss of head due to friction in a straight length of pipe depends upon (*a*) the velocity or speed of flow of the water, (*b*) the diameter of the pipe, (*c*) the length of pipe, and (*d*) the smoothness of the pipe. All these factors are included in the formula

$Lf_{100} = \dfrac{k \times v^{1\cdot 8}}{d}$ where $Lf_{100} =$ loss of head due to friction per 100 ft. of pipe, $k =$

the coefficient of friction, $d =$ the internal diameter of the pipe in inches, and v the velocity in feet per second. (The length of the pipe may, of course, be in any direction, vertical, horizontal or sloping.)

In practice the velocity is generally expressed in terms of discharge in gallons per minute, which is the usual basis upon which the designer works. In the graphs given later for pipe sizing, velocity in feet per second has been converted to flow in gallons per minute, and unless the above formula is being used there is no further need to consider velocity in terms of feet per second.

In designing pipe sizes in systems fed from pressure mains it is also necessary to convert pressure in terms of pounds per square inch into the equivalent hydraulic or static head in feet. Table IX is therefore given here for easy reference.

TABLE IX—*Conversion of Pressure into Hydraulic Head.*

Pressure	Hydraulic Head	Pressure	Hydraulic Head
lb. per sq. in.	ft.	lb. per sq. in.	ft.
10	23	80	184
20	46	90	207
30	69	100	230
40	92	125	287·5
50	115	150	345
60	138	175	402·5
70	161	200	460

As regards the smoothness of the pipes, the loss of head due to friction depends upon the factor k, which can be regarded as a coefficient for friction between the water and the pipe, and therefore, for a given combination of static head and discharge, the lower the value of k becomes, the smaller can the pipe diameter be made. k is found to be 0·86 for copper and 1·06 for iron, which gives an appreciably smaller loss of head in copper pipes than in iron pipes. Table XIV (p. 70) sets out the comparative losses of head due to friction in copper and iron pipes of various diameters for various velocities in gallons per minute, and the differences are naturally more pronounced as the velocity increases.

Allowances for Bends and Fittings

So far, only the loss of head due to friction between the water and the pipe walls has been considered. At bends, elbows, tees, valves, etc., there will be an even greater retarding effect upon the flow of water, and suitable allowances must be made for these items. These allowances are usually made in terms of additions to the actual length of pipe, and Table X gives the appropriate length of pipe, expressed in pipe diameters, to be added for the various fittings. For instance, for a 90° elbow in a 1 in. pipe, an equivalent length of 30×1 in., or $2\frac{1}{2}$ ft., must be added to the actual length of pipe.

TABLE X—*Frictional Resistance of Pipe Fittings. Approximate Allowances to be made.*

Bend or Fitting	Equivalent Length of Pipe in Pipe Diameters
90° bend (centre line radius = 1 diam.)	20
90° bend (centre line radius = 2 to 8 diams.) ..	10
90° elbows. 1 in. to 2½ in. pipes	30
90° elbows. 3 in. to 6 in. pipes	40
45° elbows. 1 in. to 3 in. pipes	15
45° elbows. 4 in. to 10 in. pipes	20
Tees. 1 in. to 4 in. pipes	60
Tee (when fluid enters branch)	90
Gate valves open	10
Globe valves open ½ in. to 2½ in.	345

Discharge Rates Required

Before the design of pipe sizes can be attempted, it is, of course, necessary to know the maximum discharges required at the various sanitary fittings, and Table XI may be taken as a guide.

TABLE XI—*Discharges required at Sanitary Fittings.*
(*Taps fully open.*)

Fittings	Discharge gallons per minute each tap
Baths (domestic buildings)	6 to 10
Baths (factories, public lavatories, etc.)	8 to 12
Shower baths	5 to 8
Lavatory basins (domestic buildings)	3 to 5
Lavatory basins (factories, etc.)	4 to 6
Sinks	3 to 5
W.C. cisterns	2 to 4
Bidets	1½ to 2

Graphs for Easy Calculations

To facilitate the calculations necessary in using the formula given on p. 63 to find the sizes of pipes necessary in any installation, the graphs on pages 71 to 73 have been prepared, and examples will be given to make plain the practical use of the graphs. The graphs cover all possible velocities (in terms of gallons per minute) that are likely to be encountered. Graph I covers the heads, velocities and pipe diameters most usually found in water supply installations in buildings in this country; Graph II deals with high velocities when loss of head is proportionately high, and may sometimes be required in conjunction with Graph I or for high pressure service work. Graph III covers a much lower range of velocities and heads and is of greater interest to heating engineers for use in connection with heating schemes in which the velocity of flow is small.

In most pipe-sizing problems, the static head (vertical drop from the water level in the tank to the fitting, or the pressure of the main in pounds per square inch) is fixed, a given discharge is taken as a basis for calculation, and the solution of the problem lies in the selection of pipes of such size and smoothness that at this required discharge the available head is just balanced by the loss of head due to friction. If the pipe sizes selected are too small, this balance will occur at some discharge which is less than that specified. If the pipes are too large, the cost of material will, of course, be increased, the discharges will be greater than those required when the taps are fully open, and wasteful adjustments of the discharges will therefore be necessary at the taps. It is also probable that over-sizing of the pipes, and consequent excess flow, in one part of a system will cause robbing of taps in other parts where the pipe sizes are not proportionately large.

Design of Pipe Sizes

For any given arrangement of pipes supplying water to various points, it may be possible to size the pipes in more than one way to obtain the required discharges, but bearing in mind that economy is important, the best system will be the one in which the pipe sizes are so arranged that the least amount of pipe material is employed to obtain the discharges required. To this end, the following rules may be taken as a guide in designing: —

(1) *Ascertain the discharge point which is most likely to be starved, and the rate of loss of head in the pipe feeding it.* This point will be the one having the smallest value for the ratio: $\dfrac{\text{Head available to be lost in friction.}}{\text{Length of pipe from source.}}$ This ratio multiplied by 100 gives the minimum loss of head due to friction per 100 ft. of pipe in the system.

(2) *This minimum rate of loss of head should not be exceeded in any part of the pipe between the discharge point—Rule (1) above—and the source (tank or main).*

(3) *Working from the source, the rate of loss of head in any system may increase, but should not be designed to diminish.*

(4) *For a balanced system, at each and every discharge point, all the head available to be lost in friction should be just absorbed in obtaining the discharge required.*

Some examples are now given to make these rules and the use of the graphs clear.

Example 1

Fig. 29 represents a simple system of light gauge copper service pipes fed from a storage tank with draw-off taps at *F*, *G* and *L*. The discharges per minute required at each tap when fully open are shown in the diagram. It is required to determine the sizes of the pipes.

In order to simplify the calculations, the allowances for the fittings, bends, etc., and the total lengths of the pipes are tabulated below.

F

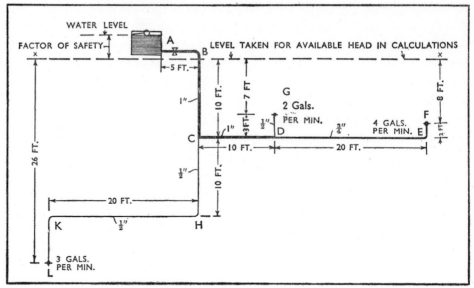

Fig. 29.

TABLE XII

TABLE XIII

ALLOWANCES FOR FITTINGS, ETC. (see Table X)		
Fitting	Assumed Diam.	Equivalent Length
	in.	ft.
Valve *A*	1	0·75
Bend *B*	1	0·75
Tee *C* (for *CF*) ..	1	7·5
Tee *C* (for *CL*) ..	½	2·5
Tee *D* (for *DF*) ..	¾	3·75
Tee *D* (for *DG*) ..	½	3·75
Bend *E* (sharp) ..	¾	1·5
Bends *H* and *K* ..	½	0·5
Tap valve *F* ..	¾	2·75
Tap valves *G* and *L*	½	1·75

LENGTHS OF PIPES			
Pipe	Length of Straight Pipe	Allowances for Fittings	Total Length
	ft.	ft.	ft.
AF	48	17	65
AD	26	9	35
DG	3	5·5	8·5
AC	16	1·5	17·5
CL	36	5·25	41·25

The discharge point most likely to be starved should first be ascertained. This point is the one having the least value for the ratio: $\dfrac{\text{Head available to be lost in friction}}{\text{Length of pipe from source}}$ (Rule 1). The total amount of static head at any discharge point is the vertical distance from the water level in the tank to the level of the discharge point, but it is not always advisable to calculate that all this head will be used up in friction since an allowance should be made for such factors as the furring of pipes, etc. In this case the head available to be lost in friction will be measured from the level of the line xx, thus providing a little more than the depth of water in the tank as a factor of safety. From the dimensions given it is clear that the point most likely to be starved is *F*. From the dimensions in the table and on the diagram the value for the above ratio for *F* is $\dfrac{8}{65}$, while for *L* the value of the ratio is $\dfrac{26}{59}$, and for *G* $\dfrac{7}{43}$. The value of the ratio for *F* being smallest, the design of the system should start from F. (If the branch CF were decreased in length and the horizontal length HK were so increased that the value of the ratio for L became smaller than that for F or G, the design of the system would be started from L.)

To find the Bore of Pipe DF.   In the 65 ft. length of pipe AF the amount of head that can be lost in friction is 8 ft. $\therefore$ the rate of loss of head in $AF = \frac{8}{65} \times 100 = 12$ ft. (approx.) per 100 ft. of pipe. This rate of loss of head should not be exceeded in any part of the pipe AF (Rule 2). The discharge required at F is 4 gallons per minute. Using Graph I, look along the bottom line to find 12 ft. head lost in 100 ft. of pipe. Read up from the point 12 on the bottom line to the sloping line marked "4 gallons per minute," and from this point on the sloping line read horizontally to the left hand vertical scale of bore in inches. It will be seen that a $\frac{3}{4}$ in. bore pipe is very slightly larger than required, but that a $\frac{1}{2}$ in. pipe would be much too small. A $\frac{3}{4}$ in. pipe is therefore selected for the length DF.

To find the Bore of Pipe CD.   Since the taps at F and G may both be turned on together and the full discharges may be required at the same time, the rate of flow required at D must be 6 gallons per minute. The rate of loss of head in CD should not exceed the 12 ft. per 100 ft. of pipe already established (Rule 2). Using Graph I as before but reading up to the sloping line marked "6 gallons per minute," it will be seen that the bore required lies between $\frac{3}{4}$ in. and 1 in., and the 1 in. bore must be employed if the full discharges are to be obtained at F and G at the same time. It can be seen from the graph that a 1 in. pipe, at the given rate of loss of head, will provide rather more than 8 gallons at D, and therefore some adjustment of the flow by the taps will be necessary if the stated discharges are not be to exceeded. This is, however, preferable to using a $\frac{3}{4}$ in. pipe, which will provide only about $4\frac{1}{2}$ gallons. If a $\frac{3}{4}$ in. pipe is used, either one or both of the taps F and G will be starved when they are turned on together.

To find the Bore of Pipe DG.   Bearing in mind Rule 4, it is advisable to calculate that all the head available at G is used up in friction at the required discharge. The amount of head lost in friction, in AD is already known and the balance must be used up in DG. The head lost in AD is at the rate of 12 ft. per 100 ft. of pipe. The length of AD is 35 ft. (from Table XIII) and therefore the actual amount of head lost in AD is $\frac{12 \times 35}{100} = 4$ ft. (approx.). The head available for G is 7 ft. and therefore the amount of head that must be lost in friction in DG is $7 - 4 = 3$ ft. From table XIII the length of DG is $8 \cdot 5$ ft. $\therefore$ the rate of loss of head in $DG = \frac{3}{8 \cdot 5} \times 100 = 35$ ft. per 100 ft. of pipe. Using Graph I, the intersection of a vertical from 35 ft. on the bottom line with the sloping line marked "2 gallons per minute" (the discharge required at G) gives a bore of between $\frac{3}{8}$ in. and $\frac{1}{2}$ in. Although providing a slightly higher discharge than required at G, the $\frac{1}{2}$ in. pipe is chosen, and because the pipe CD has already been slightly over-sized there will be no risk of G robbing F when both taps are open.

To find the Bore of Pipe AC.   If all the stated discharges at F, G and L are required at once, a flow of 9 gallons per minute is necessary at C. The bore of the pipe CD has already been fixed at 1 in. and it was seen from the graph that at the established rate of loss of head of 12 ft. per 100 ft. of pipe throughout the pipe AD a 1 in. pipe would supply approximately 9 gallons per minute, so that it is not necessary to increase the bore of AC, which is also made 1 in. There will still be sufficient flow at C to supply the full discharge of 3 gallons per minute at L when the taps F and G are open, and without robbing F and G, provided that the pipe CL is properly sized.

To find the Bore of Pipe CL.   The rate of loss of head in AC is 12 ft. per 100 ft. of pipe. The length of AC is $17 \cdot 5$ ft. $\therefore$ the amount of head used up in AC is $\frac{12 \times 17 \cdot 5}{100} = 2$ ft. (approx.). The head available for L is 26 ft., so the amount of head to be used up in friction in CL (Rule 4) is $26 - 2 = 24$ ft. The length of CL is $41 \cdot 25$ ft. $\therefore$ the rate of loss of head in $CL = \frac{24 \times 100}{41 \cdot 25} = 58$ ft. per 100 ft. of pipe (approx.). Using Graph I, the intersection of a vertical from 58 ft. on the bottom line with the sloping line marked "3 gallons per minute" (discharge required at L) gives a bore of just under

½ in. A ¾ in. pipe would be too large (allowing a discharge of 8 gallons per minute at the given rate of loss of head) and would rob either or both the taps *F* and *G*. A ½ in. pipe is therefore chosen for *CL*.

Example 2

Fig. 30 represents a system of light gauge copper supply pipes fed from a main in which the pressure is nominally 50 lb. per square inch. This pressure is equivalent to 115 ft. of head (see Table IX), and in order to allow for a possible drop in pressure, etc., the amount of head available to be used up in friction is taken as approximately 75% of the nominal static head, i.e. as 85 ft. The static head available for each discharge point is therefore taken as 85 ft. minus the vertical height of each discharge point above the

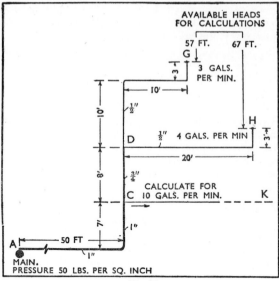

Fig. 30.

level of the main. The available static head at each discharge point is shown in the diagram.

Unless one of the branches *DH* or *CK* is very long, the point *G* is the most likely to be starved (Rule 1), and will therefore determine the rate of loss of head in the pipe from *A* to *G* (Rule 2). The total pipe length from *A* to *G* is 88 ft. of actual pipe plus allowances for bends and fittings, which can be calculated to total an extra 12 ft., making 100 ft. in all. The head available to be lost in friction in *AG* is 57 ft. and the rate of loss of head in *AG* is therefore 57 ft. per 100 ft. of pipe.

To find the Bore of Pipe DG.   Rate of loss of head = 57 ft. per 100 ft. of pipe. Discharge required = 3 gallons per minute. Using Graph I as before, the intersection of a vertical from 57 on the bottom line with the sloping line marked "3 gallons per minute" gives a bore of just under ½ in. A ½ in. pipe will actually supply about 3½ gallons per minute, but a ⅜ in. pipe will supply less than 1·5 gallons per minute, so that the ½ in. bore is chosen.

To find the Bore of Pipe CD.   If it is assumed that the stated discharges at *H* and *G* will be required at the same time, the flow necessary at *D* will be 7 gallons. The rate of loss of head due to friction in *CD* must remain 57 ft. per 100 ft. of pipe (Rules 2 and 3), and using Graph I as before, it will be seen that a ¾ in. pipe is necessary although rather too large.

To find the Bore of Pipe AC.   The stated discharges may be required at both *G* and *H* while 10 gallons is being drawn off in the branch *CK*, so that a total flow of 17 gallons is required at *C*. The rate of loss of head in *AC* must remain at 57 ft. per 100 ft. of pipe, and from Graph I it is found that a flow of just over 20 gallons is given by a 1 in. pipe, while a ¾ in. pipe will only supply about 10 gallons. The 1 in. bore is therefore used for *AC*.

To find the Bore of Pipe DH.   The amount of static head available for *H* is 67 ft. Some of this head has already been used up in friction in *AD* at the rate of 57 ft. per 100 ft. The length *AD* can be taken as 70 ft. (including allowances) and the actual amount of head used up in *AD* is therefore $\frac{57 \times 70}{100} = 40$ ft. (approx.). The amount of head that must be used up in friction in *DH* is therefore $67 - 40 = 27$ ft. (Rule 4). *DH* = 30 ft. (including allowances). The rate of loss of head in *DH* is therefore 27 ft. in 30 ft. or $\frac{27}{30} \times 100 = 90$ ft. per 100 ft. length of pipe. The discharge required at *H* is 4 gallons per minute. Graph I gives a ½ in. bore as the most suitable. A ½ in. pipe will actually deliver 5 gallons at *H*, but as the pipe *DG* has already been slightly over-sized there should be no robbing of *G* when the tap at *H* is fully open.

The size necessary for the branch *CK* would be calculated by the same method as that just employed to determine the bore of *DH*, beginning with the last discharge point on *CK*, i.e. the point most likely to be starved.

Example of the Use of Graph II. Assume that the branch *DH* in Fig. 30 is reduced to a total length of 10 ft. (including allowances). It has been calculated above that if *H* is not to rob *G* the amount of head which must be used up in friction in *DH* is 27 ft. If the length of *DH* is 10 ft. the rate of loss of head is 27 ft. in 10 ft., or $\frac{27 \times 100}{10} = 270$ ft. per 100 ft. of pipe. In this case Graph II must be used. The intersection of a vertical from 270 on the bottom line with the sloping line marked "4 gallons per minute" gives a bore of a little under $\frac{3}{8}$ in. A $\frac{3}{8}$ in. pipe would therefore be used.

Use of Graphs in checking proposed or existing systems of Copper Supply Pipes. Suppose, for instance, that in the system shown in Fig. 29 it is proposed to make the pipe from *A* to *F* of $\frac{3}{4}$ in. bore, with $\frac{1}{2}$ in. pipes for *DG* and *CL*. It is required to determine whether these sizes will produce the discharges stated in the diagram when all the taps are turned on simultaneously. If the taps are all open, flows of 9 and 6 gallons per minute are required at *C* and *D* respectively. From Graph I the rates of loss of head in a $\frac{3}{4}$ in. pipe in which there are flows of 9 and 6 gallons per minute are, respectively, 45 ft. and 20 ft. per 100 ft. of pipe. The length of *AC* = 17·5 ft. (see table in Example 1). ∴ the actual loss of head due to friction in *AC* = $\frac{45 \times 17 \cdot 5}{100}$ = 7·8 ft. The length of *CD*, including allowances, is 14 ft. ∴ the actual loss of head due to friction in *CD* = $\frac{20 \times 14}{100}$ = 2·8 ft. It is seen, therefore, that if the required discharges are to be obtained simultaneously, the static head required at *D* is 7·8 + 2·8 = 10·6 ft. This is more than the calculated available static head at *D* (10 ft.), and the required flow of 6 gallons would not therefore be obtained. The actual discharges obtained when all the taps are open will therefore be considerably less than those required, and the bores of pipes *AC* and *CD* must be increased, as was shown in Example 1. To determine whether discharges of 3 and 4 gallons per minute can be obtained simultaneously at *L* and *F* respectively the same method would be employed, taking a flow of 7 gallons per minute in *AC* and 4 gallons per minute in *CF*.

Note.

The discharges given in the examples are nominal only and are not intended to refer to any particular fittings. For the discharges required for various fittings, see Table XI, page 64.

The two systems of pipes shown in Figs. 29 and 30, although made simple for the sake of clearness, were chosen at random and the problem of designing the pipe sizes in the two systems may be said to be fairly representative of problems found in everyday practice. In arriving at the pipe sizes it has been particularly apparent that in any system absolute accuracy is extremely unlikely, since the range of bores of standard tubes is not sufficiently elastic to permit the exact discharges required to be provided. Some adjustment of flow is therefore invariably necessary at the taps if the stated discharges are not to be exceeded. This adjustment of flow at the taps resulting from a slight over-sizing of the pipes is in all cases preferable to under-sizing the pipes, which is likely to cause robbing of one tap by another. In this respect it is also advisable to consider carefully the number of taps likely to be turned on at once. In a large building, such as a block of flats, it is necessary to allow for the peak periods; to underestimate the discharges required simultaneously will result in inconvenient robbing of the supply to one flat by another.

The final minor adjustment of the discharges in a completed installation in which it is found that some taps tend to rob others may conveniently be made by screwing down the stop valves (if fitted) on the appropriate branches until a proper balance is reached. Stop valves are, in any case, desirable to facilitate repairs of taps, replacement of sanitary fittings, etc., particularly in large buildings, where to drain off a large part of the system may be very inconvenient.

TABLE XIV—*Friction of Water in Copper and Iron Pipes.*

Frictional loss in feet head of water for each 100 ft. length of pipe carrying water at the stated rate in gallons per minute. Loss of head in **copper** pipes given in **Heavy type**. Loss of head in iron pipes given in Light type.

Sizes of Pipes (Internal Diameters).

Gallons per Minute	¾ in.		½ in.		¾ in.		1 in.		1½ in.		2 in.		2½ in.		3 in.		4 in.	
0·5	**6·23**	7·70	**1·66**	2·05														
0·75	**12·9**	15·9	**3·44**	4·24														
1·0	**21·3**	26·3	**5·92**	7·30														
1·5	**44·9**	55·5	**11·97**	14·8														
2·0	**75·5**	93·2	**20·0**	24·7	**3·11**	3·84												
3·0					**6·48**	8·0												
4·0					**10·85**	13·4												
5·0					**16·22**	20·0	**4·52**	5·57										
8·0					**37·9**	46·8	**10·05**	12·4										
10·0							**15·0**	18·5	**2·33**	2·88								
20·0							**52·4**	64·7	**8·12**	10·02	**2·14**	2·64						
30·0									**16·85**	20·8	**4·45**	5·49						
40·0									**28·3**	34·9	**7·46**	9·20	**2·67**	3·17				
60·0											**15·5**	19·1	**5·55**	6·85				
80·0											**26·0**	32·1	**9·32**	11·5				
100·0													**13·9**	17·2	**6·06**	7·48		
150·0															**12·58**	15·5	**3·36**	4·15
200·0															**21·1**	26·0	**5·6**	6·82
300·0																	**11·7**	14·4

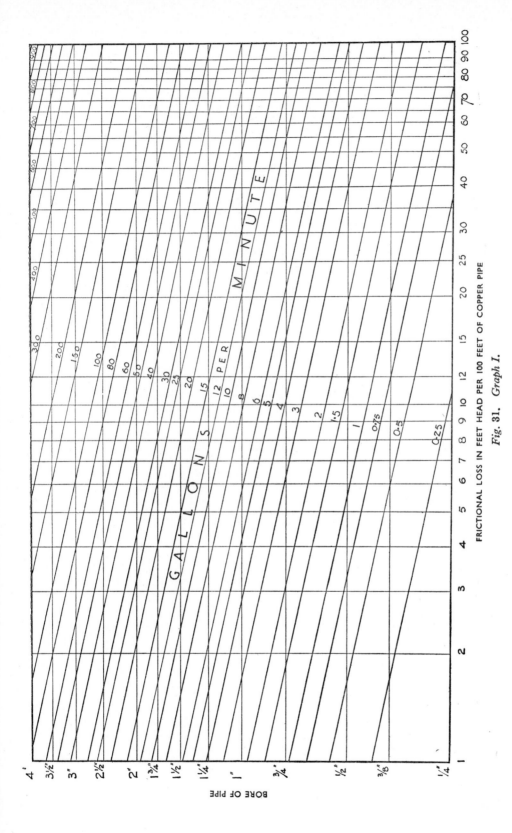

FRICTIONAL LOSS IN FEET HEAD PER 100 FEET OF COPPER PIPE

Fig. 31. Graph I.

71

72

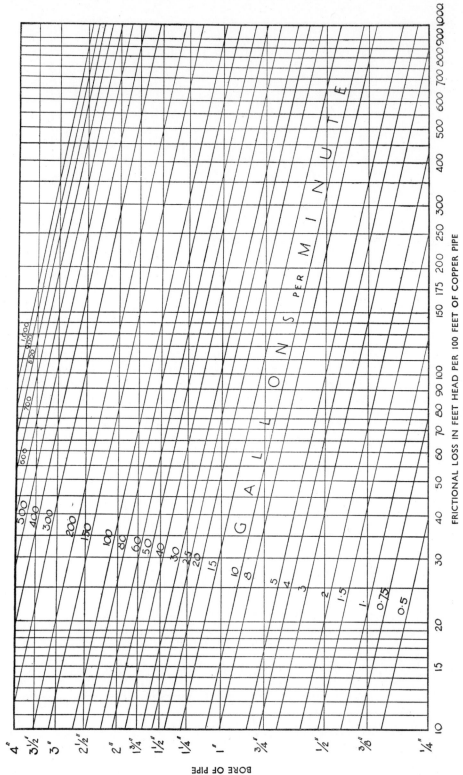

Fig. 32. *Graph II.*

BORE OF PIPE

FRICTIONAL LOSS IN FEET HEAD PER 100 FEET OF COPPER PIPE

73

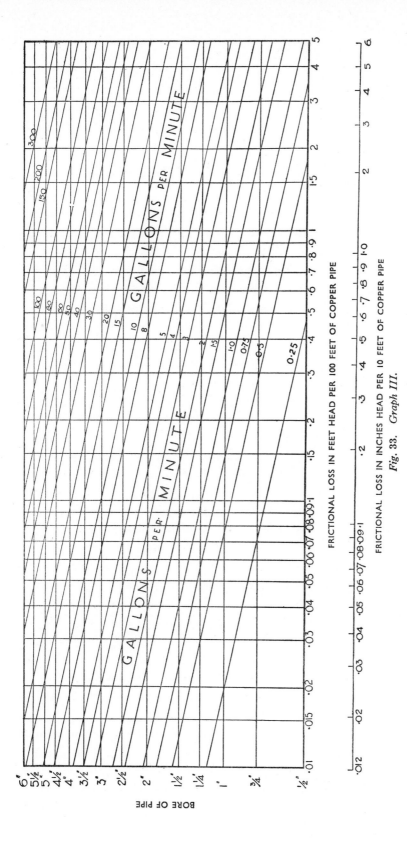

Fig. 33. *Graph III.*

CHAPTER VII

UNDERGROUND SERVICES

Brief reference has already been made to the use of copper for underground services and the matter is of sufficient importance to warrant being given further attention.

Generally speaking, the use of light gauge copper tubes for gas and water underground services was not seriously considered in this country until about 1935. Prior to that date a few local authorities allowed copper underground, but they were the exception. This was probably due to conservatism and a lack of experience with copper, for there was sufficient evidence available to show that copper and copper alloys were extremely resistant to soil corrosion.

In America and Australia the position was quite different. There major public utility companies encouraged the use of copper underground, being extremely satisfied with the behaviour of the metal even under the worst conditions. In 1946 a report was published by the British Non-Ferrous Metals Research Association, setting out the results of a series of field trials which they had conducted over a period of ten years. The conclusions arrived at were, briefly, that copper was more resistant to soil corrosion than lead in almost every class of soil. These findings confirmed the test results and practical experience gained in America and Australia over much longer periods and had the additional merit of dealing with typical soils found in this country.

The growing accumulation of evidence on the virtues of copper tubes for underground services soon led to a rapidly increasing interest in their use. This was further strengthened in 1947 by the issue of British Standard 1386, covering copper tubes suitable for installation when buried underground. So rapid has been the progress since then that almost every water authority in the country now accepts copper as a satisfactory material for underground services, while many gas undertakings are similarly using it.

Standard Sizes

Tubes of the sizes and thicknesses laid down in B.S. 1386 (see Table VI, p. 20) can be obtained in straight lengths in either soft or half-hard temper, or in coils of up to 120 ft. in length in soft temper only. For water services either half-hard or soft tube is entirely satisfactory, though for gas services, where the provision of drainage is necessary, half-hard tube is often preferred.

Corrosive Soils

There are, of course, certain acid soil conditions that would cause corrosion of any metal, even copper. Where these exist it is necessary to afford some protection to the pipe. There are various ways of doing this, the simplest being to paint the tube with bitumen, which material has been found to be very suitable and easy to apply. Alternatively the tube can be surrounded, to a distance of 6 in. or more all round, with lime-stone chippings, which have the effect of neutralizing the acidity in the soil.

The question arises as to which soils are likely to be corrosive, and it may be taken that wet ashes and clinker, red marl clay, wet decomposing matter and wet ironstone have a more or less harmful effect on all metals. Where serious corrosion occurs it is usually due to a combination of poor drainage, high sulphate and/or chloride content, a moderate or heavy rainfall and considerable moisture-retaining capacity. This last condition is necessary to allow any chemical action to take place.

It may be of interest to the reader to know that in some of the comparative tests carried out, many of the steel specimens were completely eaten away after nine years in soils similar to those just mentioned. Cast iron is almost always worse than steel, while the behaviour of wrought iron is much the same as that of steel. For further information on the resistance of copper to soil corrosion, the reader is referred to C.D.A. publication No. 40, *Copper Underground: Its Resistance to Soil Corrosion.*

Copper tubes are adequately strong to resist all normal shocks or crushing loads likely **Strength of** to be experienced when buried underground and cases of failure of buried copper tubes **Copper** are almost unknown. In this connection, it is interesting to compare the performance **Tubes** of copper and lead under piercing tests (see Table XV). The pipes used in this test were ordinary samples of pipe taken from stock. A weighted steel punch was dropped down a vertical guide from a given height on to the selected piece of tube and the effect measured. Samples of both copper and lead pipes were thus tested, and while in the case of the lead pipes every one was punctured, no penetration of a copper tube occurred. The full results of the tests are set out below.

TABLE XV—*Piercing Tests.*

| Nominal Bore | Copper | | Lead | Blow | REMARKS | |
	Temper	S.W.G.	Weight		Copper	Lead
in. $\frac{1}{2}$	Half-hard	18	lb./yd. 7	ft./lb. 9·6	Slight flattening	Pierced
$\frac{1}{2}$	Soft	18	7	8·25	Slight flattening	Pierced
$\frac{3}{4}$	Half-hard	18	9	11	Slight damage	Pierced
$\frac{3}{4}$	Soft	18	9	9·6	Some flattening and slight damage	Pierced
1	Half-hard	17	9	11	Very slight damage	Pierced
1	Soft	17	9	9·6	Some flattening and slight damage	Pierced

Owing to the trouble and expense caused by the necessity for periodically renewing **Australian** corroded galvanised wrought iron service pipes, the Metropolitan Water, Sewerage and **Experience**

Drainage Board of Sydney, Australia, decided that from 1st March, 1926 all new or replaced water services from the mains to the meter or stopcock near the building line should be laid in solid drawn copper tube. With minor exceptions this was rigidly adhered to for six and a half years, when it was made permissible under certain special conditions to use bituminous-lined galvanised water piping.

From March 1st, 1926, till July 1938, 138,000 copper services, representing 5,500,000 ft. of copper tubing, were installed in Sydney and until June, 1949, only nine services had become defective—two due to split piping—and seven due to stray current corrosion. The thickness of the piping used is shown in the following table.

TABLE XVI

Nominal outside diameter (ins.)	$\frac{3}{8}$	$\frac{1}{2}$	$\frac{13}{16}$	$1\frac{1}{32}$	$1\frac{5}{8}$	$1\frac{7}{8}$
S.W.G. ..	16	14	13	12	12	12
Inches ..	0·064	0·080	0·092	0·104	0·104	0·104

The experience of the Sydney Water Board since 1938 is that copper is the best material for buried water service pipes so far as Sydney water and soil are concerned, and the almost complete freedom from leaks indicates the effective resistance of copper to soil corrosion, in addition to its resistance to internal corrosion by the water.

Town mains, for gas and water, are usually of cast iron or steel, and the method of making a connection with light gauge copper tube presents no problem. Mains ferrules with the outlet end suitable for either compression or capillary joints are readily available. Fig. 34 shows a ferrule screwed into the cast iron main and the copper tube connected to it. Alternatively, a male iron-to-copper bend may be used.

In laying the copper, it is advisable to form a slow bend in the tube adjacent to the ferrule; this allows for any settlement in the ground and prevents damage to the screwed joint due to heavy traffic. Where the connection is made by means of a bent connector, the angle of the slow bend should be such that any downward movement tends to tighten the screwed joint between main and fitting.

Coming away from the main the copper service should be run at about 2 ft. to 2 ft. 6 in. deep so as to be out of reach of the effects of prolonged frost, and this depth must be maintained up to the point at which the service enters the building. Near the building line a copper alloy stopcock should be fitted in a stoneware pipe or brick chamber, surmounted with a cast iron cover. Inside the building a further stopcock should be fitted and if conditions allow, a drain cock also, so that the installation can be completely drained if necessary.

Laying by Mole-Plough   As has already been mentioned, soft temper copper tube to B.S. 1386–1947 can be obtained in coils of long length and the strength and flexibility of such tube enables it

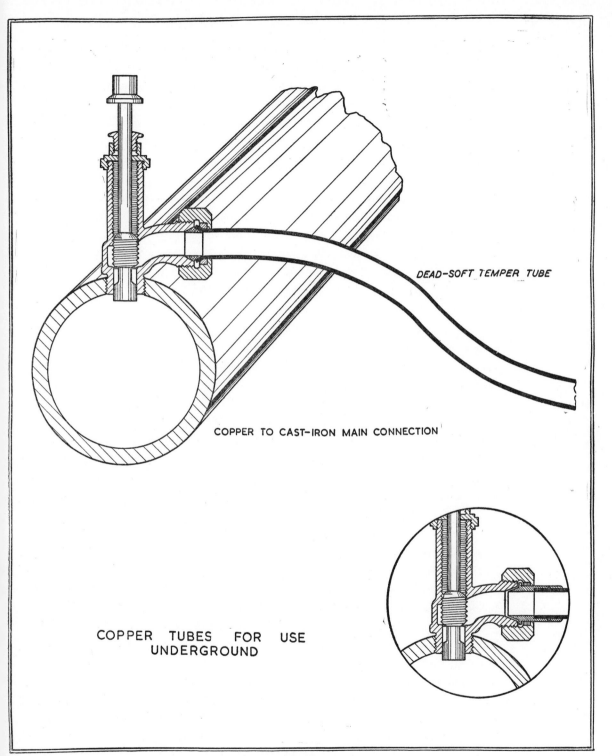

DEAD-SOFT TEMPER TUBE

COPPER TO CAST-IRON MAIN CONNECTION

COPPER TUBES FOR USE
UNDERGROUND

Fig. 34.

to be installed in suitable circumstances by "mole-ploughing." The technique of this form of pipe laying is simple and because it does away with the necessity for trench digging, long copper underground water or gas services can be laid quickly and for a fraction of the cost hitherto associated with underground pipe runs.

The principle of a "mole-plough" is the pulling through the earth of a steel bobbin, pointed at the forward end, at a predetermined depth, by either a tractor or stationary winch and endless cable. The bobbin or mole is attached to the bottom of a vertical knife or cutter projecting downwards from the carriage. To the back of the mole a stranded cable is attached, to which the copper tube is secured, so that when the carriage moves over the ground the tube is drawn into the small hole made by the mole. The depth of the mole is adjusted by raising or lowering the knife before starting, and Fig. 35 illustrates how it works. Plates XIII and XIV show a plough in operation laying a copper service pipe. The total length of this service was 850 yards and in laying, the copper was drawn underground at a speed of 120 feet per minute. Speeds of up to 150 feet per minute are not uncommon and the work can be carried out even in stony soils.

Joints in copper tube laid in this manner can be made with either manipulative compression or capillary soldered fittings. The ease and speed with which these joints can be completed make them very suitable for this work, but welding or hard-soldering can be used if so desired.

Threading Copper Through Old Steel Pipes   Another instance of how the use of soft copper tube can reduce the cost of underground services is the increasing use of such tube for threading through old iron service pipes, which procedure again avoids much trench digging. The old iron pipe is first cleaned by pulling a stiff wire brush through to remove scale deposits. A strong wire cable is then drawn in, one end of which is attached to a winch and the other to the copper tube secured by a hook bolt. The winch is set in motion and the wire rope and copper tube hauled through the old pipe (see Plate XV, facing page 81).

The great advantage of this method lies in the fact that services can be relaid under roads and pavements with a minimum of disturbance or the consequent heavy charges for making good.

Experience of authorities replacing services in this manner has proved that a copper tube one size smaller than the original iron pipe gives adequate service.*

Generally, in this country the lengths of pipe runs laid through existing iron pipes have not exceeded about 60 ft. In America, however, runs of up to 300 yards have been installed; because of the small clearance between the inside of the iron pipe and the outside of the copper tube capillary soldered joints have been used.

When the use of copper tubes run through iron barrels is being considered the question of corrosion often arises, but there need be no fear of such corrosion damaging the copper tube. Any electrolytic action taking place will result in the further corrosion of the already deteriorated iron pipe and no harm will be caused to the copper. In fact, the presence of the surrounding iron pipe will act as a complete protection for the copper tube, with

---

* The reader is referred to a paper by H. E. F. Heath, M.Inst.G.E., A.M.I.H.V.E., read before the Institution of Gas Engineers, June, 1949.

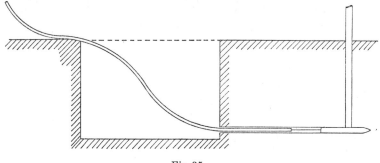

Fig. 35.

the result, as might be expected, that there has been no reported instance of a copper tube failing when so installed.

The types of joints used for underground services, are, in general, compression joints, capillary soldered joints, silver soldered, bronze or autogenously welded joints. When a compression joint is used with soft tube, one of the manipulative type (i.e. one in which the end of the tube is preformed to a cup or cone shape) should be employed.

When capillary soldered joints are used with soft copper tubes, care must be taken to ensure that the tube end is truly circular and a tube sizing tool should be used before making the joint.

Capillary Fittings Used with Soft Copper Tubes

The most important matter for consideration is not the type of joint but the material of which it is made. The material should have a resistance to corrosion by the soil in which it is to be buried not much inferior to that of copper.

Where brass has been known from experience with stopcocks and ferrules to give satisfactory service underground in any area, the alloy can safely be used for pipe joints. Where, however, any trouble has been experienced with brass, either the metal must be protected, for instance with a bituminous coating, or a more corrosion-resisting alloy be specified. Suitable alloys for use in such cases include the following compositions (Table XVII).

TABLE XVII

Per Cent			
Copper	Tin	Zinc	Lead
88	10	2	—
88	8	4	—
86	7	5	2
85	5	5	5
83	7	5	5

The filler rod used for bronze welding should have a tin content of about 5%, whilst a copper-phosphorus or copper-silver-phosphorus (Type 6, B.S. 1845–1952) filler rod would be satisfactory for use with either purpose-made capillary sockets or expanded tube ends formed with the special tools shown on page 34. Wrought copper fittings or autogenously welded joints can, of course, also be used. Before commencing to make any type of joint on soft copper tube it is always advisable to "size" the end to ensure that it is truly circular; this is particularly important when capillary fittings are used.

PLATE XIV.

PLATE XIII.

Mole plough in operation. (*See p.* 78.)

PLATE XV.   *Feeding soft copper tube into old iron pipe.*   (See p. 78.)

CHAPTER VIII

COLD WATER SERVICES

In the Introduction the many advantages of light gauge copper tubes for water services have been discussed and it would be redundant to repeat them. However, there is one particular point of interest to readers that does call for amplification. On page 10 it is stated that copper pipes "will not contaminate drinking water," which means that water conveyed in copper tubes is not affected from a health point of view by contact with the metal. It is very important that this should be known and appreciated. In the past it has been feared by some that copper might be poisonous and therefore a danger to health. There are, however, no grounds whatever for such a fear, as has been amply demonstrated both by experience and by research work on the subject. As long ago as 1925 the late Dr. J. C. Thresh, M.D., D.Sc., F.I.C., a well-known authority on water and health, carried out an investigation on the use of copper pipes with domestic hot and cold waters. His findings were published in the *Lancet* on March 28, 1925, p. 675, and were summarised as follows:—

"(1) That copper is far less acted upon by water than either iron or lead.

(2) That copper being vastly less deleterious than lead, copper pipes are far safer than lead pipes.

(3) That copper pipes can be used for all waters that are not acid in reaction.

(4) That acid waters should never be used until the acidity has been removed by treatment. Having been so treated, copper service pipes can be used.

(5) That practically all waters take up traces of copper if allowed to stand sufficiently long therewith, but that under all ordinary circumstances the amount of copper taken up is far too small to endanger health."

Other research workers have since substantiated these findings and it is now known that copper, so far from being harmful to health, is, in small quantities, an essential ingredient of our diet.

There are few, if any, public water supplies in this country with which copper cannot be used entirely satisfactorily, since such supplies are invariably treated to remove any excess acidity before being delivered to the mains. There are, however, some private water supplies derived from wells, boreholes and streams which are excessively corrosive and which will vigorously attack any metal. Such waters are plumbo-solvent and would give rise to the danger of lead poisoning if carried in lead pipes, or to rapid and excessive rusting if iron pipes were used. In such conditions, copper is the only safe material to employ if the water is not to be treated before use as recommended above.

Although untreated corrosive waters when carried in copper pipes do not constitute a danger to health, they may have a sufficiently solvent action on the copper to produce a green coloration when an alkali such as soap is added. This coloration is caused by minute traces of copper in solution in the water and usually appears in the form of green stains upon sanitary fittings, due to the dripping of a tap, or the green staining of cloths, sponges, etc., used with soapy water. While these stains may be inconvenient, they are perfectly harmless, because the amount of copper in solution in the water is much too small to be in any way dangerous to health, and cases of poisoning by copper picked up by water conveyed in copper tubes are unknown.

Green staining is more likely to occur with hot water than with cold, because the heating of an acid water generally increases its solvent action. Green stains on sanitary fittings, cloths, sponges, etc., can be removed by washing with a dilute solution (5 per cent by volume) of hydrochloric acid, but care should be taken to rinse the article afterwards with a dilute soda solution and clean water.

Green staining sometimes occurs in a new installation during its first period of use, while the protective oxidised film is being formed on the inside of the pipes by the oxygen dissolved in the water. As the film forms staining usually subsides, but if it persists to a considerable extent it is a useful warning, not given by lead pipes, that the water is unduly corrosive and is not suitable for conveyance in pipes of any metal without preliminary treatment.

Treatment of Acid Waters

In cases of persistent green staining an examination of the water is desirable to ascertain the most suitable treatment to correct the acidity, which may be due to organic acids, such as those found in waters from peaty catchment areas, or to the presence of free carbonic acid. Acidity of both kinds may be neutralised by dosing with an alkali such as lime, a treatment which is widely adopted in both private and public supplies. It is important that lime dosing should be accurately controlled, particularly when the acid content of the water varies from time to time, due, for instance, to the varying amount of rainfall in peaty areas where the water collected in reservoirs tends to become increasingly acid during wet periods. In such cases, the lime dosage must be varied so that the acidity is neutralised sufficiently without adding excess lime liable to cause unnecessary scale in hot water pipes. Dosing with soda ash, which does not increase the hardness of the water, is also sometimes used. Alternative methods are to filter the water through coarsely ground limestone, magnesite, or chalk.

If the acidity of a water is due only to the presence of free carbonic acid it may be treated by any of the methods already described, or up to 90 per cent. of the free CO_2 may be removed by aeration. Aeration plants are obtainable in sizes suitable for small country house supplies from wells or for much larger water supplies, but they cannot be arranged to work under pressure. In cases where it is desirable to remove CO_2 from water supplied from a main, it is therefore sometimes preferable to employ a magnesite filter which can work under pressure and which takes up less space than the aeration apparatus. The advantages of the aeration process are that no hardness is added to the water and that if the amount of CO_2 varies the process is not affected, whereas with lime dosing, as already described, the dosing must be carefully controlled to meet such variations.

The majority of waters sufficiently acid to attack copper appreciably are very soft, so that the addition of some hardness by lime dosing or filtration through limestone or magnesite may not be undesirable. It should not be supposed, however, that hardness is necessarily an indication of freedom from acidity, because occasionally a hard water is found which is definitely plumbo-solvent and which may also have a solvent action upon copper. Such waters usually have a hardness principally of the permanent type, which does not give a protection to the inside of pipes by the formation of scale, and derive their acidity from free carbonic acid or a high content of nitrates.

Readers are reminded of the analytical service outlined in the Introduction to this book, (see p. 12) which is free to responsible individuals and bodies. If there is any doubt as to the suitability of a water for conveyance in copper pipes, or if green staining continues after an initial period of use, the Association will, if necessary, arrange for an analysis of the water to be made by independent and authoritative analysts, so that the nature of the water and its action on copper may be accurately determined. The results of the analysis and any tests which may be carried out are placed at the disposal of the enquirer, together with any relevant comments or recommendations which the Association may be able to make. In cases where the treatment of the water is considered desirable, the Association is also prepared to advise as to the most suitable form of treatment to be applied.

C.D.A. Analytical Service

The use of copper cold water storage tanks is not so universal as that of copper tubes, although copper tanks are widely used in districts where the water is of such an acid character that galvanised iron tanks, as well as iron tubes, have a very short life, due to excessive rusting, and lead tanks are unsafe because of the danger of lead poisoning. In these districts it has been usual to employ copper-lined wood tanks with brazed or bronze welded seams, and such tanks are permitted by most water authorities. There are now also obtainable 40-gallon and 60-gallon copper storage tanks made up with welded or brazed seams, which are sufficiently strong to be self-supporting.

Copper Tubes with Iron Tanks and Cisterns

With the majority of waters the use of galvanised iron or steel storage tanks with copper tubes is perfectly satisfactory. Without going deeply into the highly involved subject of electrolytic or galvanic action, it may be mentioned, however, that trouble has been known to occur as a result of particles of iron or iron rust from old or imperfectly galvanised or bower-barffed tanks being washed into the copper tubes, setting up local centres of corrosion, perhaps resulting eventually in pitting. Corrosion caused by iron rust is not likely to occur in the service pipe from a main, or even in the ordinary distributing service, owing to the comparatively high velocity of flow which prevents the particles of iron rust from lodging in the bottom of horizontal pipes, but it has been known to occur, for instance, in large-diameter ring heating mains in which the velocity of the water is low, and in copper hot water cylinders. On the other hand, accelerated corrosion of galvanised iron cold water tanks might be caused in isolated cases by minute traces of copper in solution in the water, as might occur with a water of an acid character after passing through a copper service pipe from the main. This accelerated corrosion of galvanised iron is, however, more likely to occur in hot water storage tanks or cylinders, since the amount of copper taken into solution is usually greater when the water is heated and its action on the cylinder increased by repeated circulation. The risks of corrosion of copper tubes and copper cylinders by iron rust, and the corrosion of galvanised iron tanks by traces of copper in solution, are naturally greater if the water is definitely corrosive to metals, and careful consideration should be given to the probable action of a water before a mixture of the two metals is incorporated in an installation.

In any case of doubt, a reliable precaution which adds only a very small percentage to the total cost is to adopt an all-copper installation in which the cold storage tank, as well as the hot storage cylinder, is of copper. If, however, iron tanks are to be used with an acid water, a partial remedy is to have them coated, for instance, with Dr. Angus Smith's solution, a black bituminous compound applied hot. All iron filings and chippings should be carefully removed from storage tanks after connection is made to them. Iron nails left in galvanised iron tanks have been known to cause perforation.

Internal Cleanliness of Tubes

Great care is taken by manufacturers to ensure that the interiors of copper tubes are absolutely clean before the tubes are sent out from the factory. It is important that this internal cleanliness should be maintained until the tubes are finally installed, since it is possible that occasional failures of water tubes by perforation may be due to particles of foreign matter which have gained access to the tubes before installation and have adhered to the interior surfaces. It is therefore strongly recommended that care should be taken to prevent dirt, dust, or other matter from entering the tubes during transit, while on the site, and during installation.

Precautions Against Bursting During Frost

In the Introduction to this book it is stated that the internal smoothness and ductility of copper tubes are factors in reducing the risk of bursts in frost. A frost-burst is due to the expansion of the water as it freezes, and a burst is likely to occur when freezing water is trapped between two ice plugs or between an ice plug and a dead end, stop-valve, tap, etc. The smoothness of copper pipes allows an ice plug to be pushed along the tube by the expanding water, and the ductility allows a little "give" in the tube walls. This is not to say that copper tubes will not burst in frost under certain conditions. If the pipe-line is not properly protected, bursts will occur whatever the metal. It is therefore necessary to take proper precautions in the laying and fixing of cold water services. Suitable and simple precautions may be briefly summarised as follows:—

(1) Underground pipes, as stated earlier, should be buried at least 2 ft. underground.

(2) Service pipes from the mains should be taken into the building at the same depth underground and should not be allowed to appear in the open.

(3) The rising main to the cistern should be carried up on a warm inner wall.

(4) In roof spaces the pipes should be suitably lagged, and the storage tank should be insulated by surrounding it with a wooden casing 3 in. or 4 in. clear of the tank and packed with sawdust or other insulating material. The storage tank should also have a wooden top.

(5) The running of cold water services adjacent to hot water or heating pipes, and the placing of the storage tank near a chimney in the roof space, are additional protection, which, of course, is only effective when the building is in normal use.

CHAPTER IX

HOT WATER SUPPLY

Light gauge copper tubing is admirably suited to the conveyance of hot water, not only for domestic purposes but also for heating apparatus designed for warming rooms and corridors by means of radiators or panels, etc. The chief advantages of copper are that (1) the relatively small outer diameter is more easily housed in confined spaces; (2) the reduced outer area loses less heat by radiation, and the smaller mass of metal involved saves time and heat loss when warming up; (3) there can be no rust from the pipes to discolour the tap water; (4) scale does not cling so easily to the smoother bore of copper primary circulation pipes in a hard water district, and if it does form is more readily removed; (5) nodules of growths of rust cannot occur to choke the bore in copper pipes as they do, even with galvanised iron, in soft water districts; (6) the work of fitting is infinitely less laborious than is entailed in cutting and screwing iron pipe, and is cleaner and more interesting; (7) the pipes are easily assembled and readily taken down if required, for instance, to scale the primary flow, as is necessary periodically in hard water districts, or to wash out sediment; (8) copper's rigidity makes the pipes self-supporting over considerable spans; they also have a neater appearance when properly fixed, and of course require no painting, thus saving a recurring expense.

This book does not set out to be a treatise on the design of hot water supply installations, but it is thought advisable for general reference to illustrate the two main types of installation: (a) the system in which the water in the cylinder is directly heated by the boiler, and (b) the indirect system in which the water in the cylinder or calorifier is heated by means of a pipe coil or immersed heater. These two systems are shown in Figs. 36 and 37, and it is assumed that the reader already knows or can find out elsewhere the advantages and disadvantages of the two systems.

For installations of either type, light gauge copper tubes jointed by any of the methods indicated in Chapter III, together with copper cylinders and calorifiers, are eminently suitable, for the reasons set out above, and it is intended here to describe the points in the design of an installation which are particularly relevant to the use of copper.

Boilers and Radiators

In certain districts where the water is very soft and is particularly corrosive to iron, copper back boilers have long been used, and in Scotland copper independent boilers are also sometimes employed. The usual method of overcoming the difficulty of a water which is corrosive to iron is to employ the indirect method of heating the water with a calorifier, so that the water in contact with the iron boiler is not frequently changing.

86

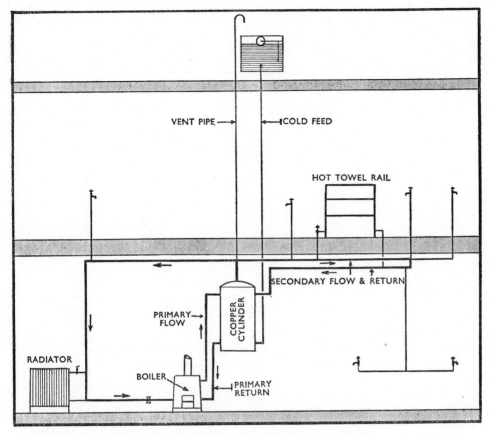

Fig. 36. *Typical "direct" hot water supply installation.*

The corrosion of the iron boiler is therefore limited to the attack of the first charge of water and is not continuous.

If with a "direct" system an occasional radiator be installed in conjunction with the hot water supply circuit of copper tubes, as shown in Fig. 36, and if the water is soft and likely to attack cast iron, it is essential that the radiator be also of copper. Copper radiators are discussed in Chapter X (see p. 94). For the general run of water supplies, however, a bower-barffed cast iron boiler and radiators in a direct system will prove satisfactory with copper pipes. With an indirect system it is, of course, safe in all cases to use an iron boiler and radiator with copper pipes.

For connections to cylinders, boilers and radiators the usual straight or bent couplings, "iron thread to light gauge copper compression or capillary soldered fittings," should be used, even if welding or brazing is used for the other joints (see Figs. 3, 4, and 7, pp. 22, 24 and 27, for fittings). Such an arrangement permits the installation to be taken down easily for adjustments or repairs to the units, and for scaling or clearing out sediment.

**Connections
to Boilers,
etc.**

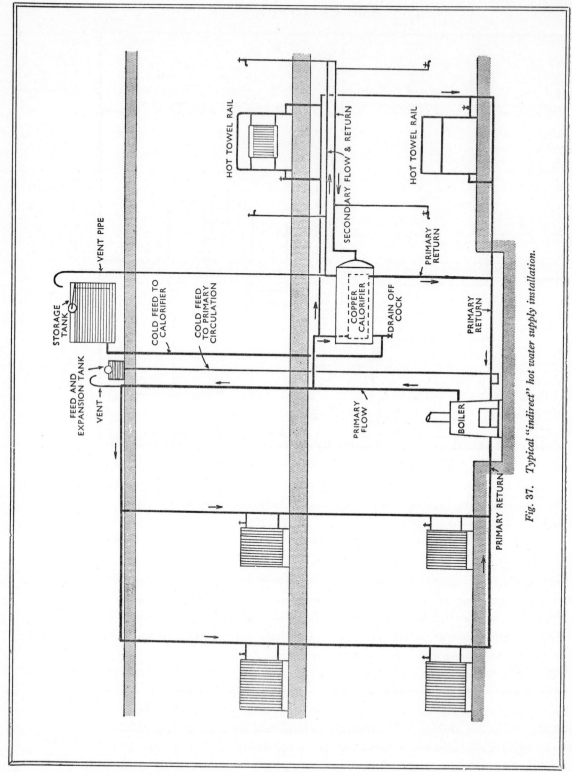

STORAGE TANK

VENT PIPE

FEED AND EXPANSION TANK

VENT

COLD FEED TO CALORIFIER

COLD FEED TO PRIMARY CIRCULATION

PRIMARY FLOW

BOILER

HOT TOWEL RAIL

SECONDARY FLOW & RETURN

COPPER CALORIFIER

DRAIN OFF COCK

PRIMARY RETURN

PRIMARY RETURN

HOT TOWEL RAIL

PRIMARY RETURN

Fig. 37.   Typical "indirect" hot water supply installation.

It should be noted that copper is attacked by sulphurous fumes when allied with condensed moisture, so that copper pipes should not be exposed in such positions as the flues of a fireback boiler. If this cannot be avoided, means should be adopted to protect them with brickwork, asbestos sleeves or fireclay. **Copper Pipes in Flues**

Although in many cases galvanised iron cylinders may safely be used in conjunction with copper pipes, it is known that some waters, such as those containing an appreciable amount of free CO_2, may take into solution minute traces of copper, and although the action is not in any way harmful to the copper pipes and may not be sufficient to cause green staining, it may nevertheless cause accelerated corrosion of galvanised iron and steel hot water cylinders (see p. 83). It is therefore strongly recommended that a copper cylinder, which adds little to the cost of the installation, should be employed with copper pipes in any cases of doubt, so that all risk of this trouble may be avoided. **Cylinders**

The British Standard for Copper Cylinders for Domestic Purposes (No. 699–1951) provides for the material, method of manufacture, thickness and dimensions, amount of dish in ends (i.e. radius of curvature = three-quarters of the diameter of barrel), testing requirements, marking, connections, etc., and Table XVIII, taken from the Specification, is reproduced with the permission of the British Standards Institution (see p. 91). The Specification states that all cylinders shall be provided with a screwed connection for a circulator or immersion heater, and fixes the positions of all connections. Electrical immersion heaters for use with these copper cylinders should conform to the requirements of the British Standard for Electric Water Heaters (No. 843–1939).

In the indirect system shown in Fig. 37, the tap water is heated by the immersed heater within the cylinder, which is then usually termed a calorifier. This heater must have an appropriately large area of conducting surface if it is to be effective, and because copper is the best conductor of heat of all the common metals, it should preferably be employed. **Indirect Cylinders**

British Standard 1566–1949 covers copper indirect cylinders and specifies sizes and all important manufacturing and design details, including the sizes and positions of all connections.

Table XVIII on p. 91 gives the sizes of cylinders standardised and the minimum thickness of copper to be used in their manufacture. The Standard specifies that all seams shall be brazed and gives various alternative arrangements for the accommodation of electric immersion heaters.

Fig. 38 shows a sectional view of an indirect cylinder in a vertical position. The sketch also shows the method of connecting up the primary flow and return pipes. The immersed heater shown is a double-walled cylinder of copper, but the heating element is often in the form of a copper pipe coil or battery of copper pipes. Copper coils or heaters are used in galvanised iron or steel cylinders, but if the nature of the water is at all open to suspicion, it is essential for the body of the calorifier to be of copper also.

Fig. 39 shows a steam coil of copper tube built into a cylinder to form a steam-heated calorifier. Owing to the high thermal conductivity of copper, such a calorifier is very efficient because of the rapid transmission of heat through the copper coil to the water in which it is immersed. Where steam services exist in a building, it is a very convenient and economical means of producing hot water for tap supply. A boiler of the ordinary type is not needed unless the steam supply is intermittent. In that case the ordinary boiler and primary circulation pipes can be put in as a stand-by. An automatic shut-off, actuated by a thermostat, is advisable to prevent overheating or boiling of water in the cylinder, and can be adjusted to shut off at any desired temperature; 160° F. to 180° F. is sufficient for ordinary requirements and such a temperature avoids scaling or furring up of the inner walls and outer surface of the steam coil.

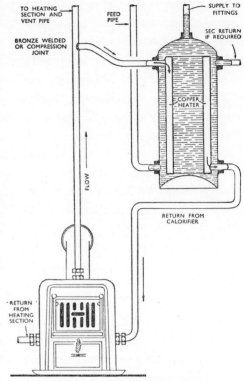

Fig. 38. A copper calorifier in an "indirect" hot water supply installation.

The British Standard for Calorifiers (No. 853–1939) standardises the design and materials of copper calorifiers and of the copper heating elements in steel and iron calorifiers.

Electric and Gas Water Heaters

Electric hot water heaters provide an efficient and economical method of obtaining hot water, particularly where it is required only intermittently. These heaters are of two main types; those through which the water is delivered simply by gravity, and those which work under pressure. They consist of a copper cylinder or container in which is mounted an electric heating element, and, as already mentioned, there is a British Standard (No. 843) for these heaters. The fact that copper, tinned on the inside, has been standardised for the cylindrical or rectangular containers makes

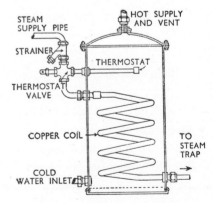

Fig. 39. A steam coil calorifier.

these heaters particularly suitable for use with a copper tube installation.

Because copper has a high thermal conductivity it is extensively used in the construction of gas-fired geysers and water heaters, the body of the geyser and the pipe coil within it being formed of copper sheet and tube respectively.

Copper and brass towel rails (plated if required) may be obtained ready made, or can be made up quite easily by welding or silver soldering or by the use of capillary soldered fittings.

Towel Rails

TABLE XVIII—*Copper Cylinders for Domestic Purposes (B.S. 699–1951).*

British Standard size number†	Dimensions		Actual Capacity	Thickness of copper sheet					
				Grade 1		Grade 2		Grade 3	
				Test pressure: 70 lb. per sq. in. Max. working head of water: 100 ft.*		Test pressure: 40 lb. per sq. in. Max. working head of water: 60 ft.*		Test pressure: 20 lb. per sq. in. Max. working head of water: 30 ft.*	
	External diameter	External height (over) dome)	(See Clause 4e)‡	Body and end dished outwards	End dished inwards	Body and end dished outwards	End dished inwards	Body and end dished outwards	End dished inwards
	A	B							
	In.	In.	Gal.	S.W.G.	S.W.G.	S.W.G.	S.W.G.	S.W.G.	S.W.G.
1	14	36	17¼	17	15	20	17	22	18
2	16	36	22¼	16	14	19	16	22	18
3	18	27	20	15	13	18	15	22	18
4	18	30	22¾	15	13	18	15	22	18
5	18	33	25¼	15	13	18	15	22	18
6	18	36	28	15	13	18	15	22	18
7	18	42	33¼	15	13	18	15	22	18
8	21	48	52¼	13	11	17	14	21	16
9	24	48	67½	12	10	16	13	18	14
10	24	63	91	12	10	16	13	18	14

* The working head shall be measured from the bottom of the cylinder.
† Cylinders should be ordered according to the B.S. size number.
‡ The actual capacities given above are the figures for cold water, and do not indicate the quantity of hot water which can be drawn off.

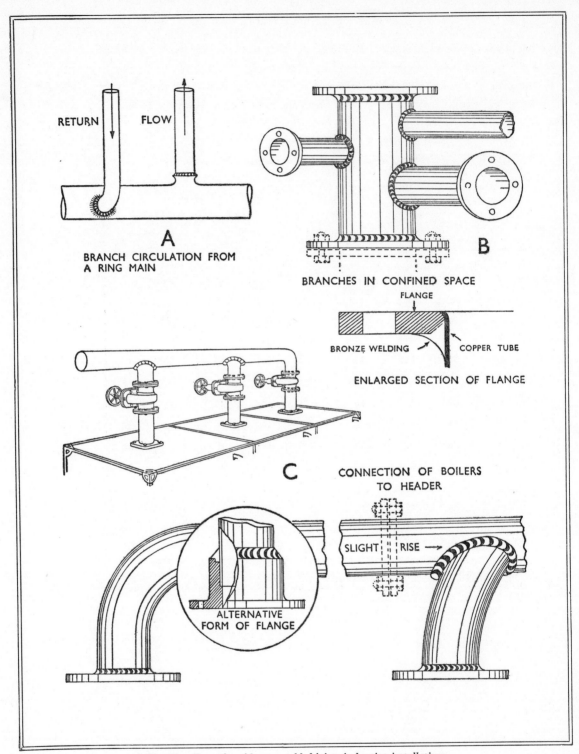

RETURN   FLOW

A

BRANCH CIRCULATION FROM
A RING MAIN

B

BRANCHES IN CONFINED SPACE

FLANGE

BRONZE WELDING   COPPER TUBE

ENLARGED SECTION OF FLANGE

C

CONNECTION OF BOILERS
TO HEADER

SLIGHT   RISE →

ALTERNATIVE
FORM OF FLANGE

Fig. 40.   Examples of bronze welded joints in heating installations.

CHAPTER X

HEATING INSTALLATIONS

In the past, heavy or medium gauge copper tubes were used extensively for hot water work and heating installations. There usually being no need for such strong tubes, they have been superseded to a large extent by light gauge tubes, the advantages of which, as set out in previous chapters, apply equally to all types of heating installations.

As in hot water supply work, the method of jointing used is generally by compression or capillary soldered fittings or by bronze welding, although hard or silver soldering is sometimes used. On very large installations it is not uncommon to find that joints in all the pipes over 1 in. are welded, compression or capillary fittings being used for the jointing of the smaller sizes of tube. By adopting such methods the cost of the job may often be kept to the minimum. Obviously welding has special advantages; for example, where branches leave headers, when flow and return are generally close to each other but at varying angles. The advantage of welding such joints is, of course, that they can be fabricated on site easily as required, whereas with other methods expensive fittings would be needed. The illustration A, Fig. 40 is an instance where welding is used as stated above. Fig. 40, B illustrates a similar application of welding for jointing branches into the main riser. C in the same figure shows welded connections for a battery of boilers joined in series.

Jointing

In heating installations, as in other types of installation where there are long lengths of pipe in which stresses due to thermal expansion and contraction are unrelieved by bends or offsets, it may be necessary to provide for movement by fitting expansion loops or joints, suitable types of which have already been described in Chapter V, p. 60.

The question is sometimes raised of the danger from galvanic or electrolytic action arising from the use of copper tubes with cast iron radiators. Except in the case of waters of a very corrosive nature, the danger in these circumstances is virtually non-existent, since the replenishment of water in a closed circuit system only takes place at infrequent intervals. When charging a system with water which is originally of a very acid character, the water should be treated by lime dosage or otherwise, as already described in connection with cold water services (see Chapter VIII, p. 82). With the majority of waters the safety of the practice of employing cast iron radiators is borne out by the very large number of cases in which they have been in service with copper pipes for many years without trouble. In fact, one of the largest firms of heating engineers in the world is now making extensive use of light gauge copper tubes, joined with capillary fittings, in conjunction with cast iron radiators. Conversely, iron pipes have often been connected

Corrosion

93

to copper coils, and (in the U.S.A.) to copper radiators, without trouble being experienced.

Copper Radiators and Convectors

Radiators of conventional type are obtainable in copper if required, and although more expensive in first cost than those of cast iron they may be necessary in certain cases, as, for instance, when installed in the circulation of a direct hot water supply installation in which the water is known to be corrosive to iron (see also Plate XXVI, facing p. 113).

It is of interest that finned copper convection heaters are manufactured which, owing to the very high conductivity of copper, greatly increase the amount of convected heat per unit area. These heaters, which may be built into a flue or panel in a wall so that an air draught is induced through the heater, consist briefly of horizontal finned copper tubes fixed into bronze end tanks. A typical design uses copper tubes of $\frac{5}{8}$ in. outside diameter with a wall thickness of $0 \cdot 025$ in., on to which a copper strip $\frac{5}{16}$ in. wide by $0 \cdot 012$ in. thick is wound in a spiral with about 7 turns to the inch and is soldered in position. Alternatively, the spiral strip is knurled into a spiral groove cut into the wall of the tube, or the fins may be formed by rolling from a thick copper tube.

Forced Circulation

In large low-pressure heating installations it is necessary to assist the circulation of the heated water by installing a centrifugal pump near the boiler. The pump is usually "direct-coupled" to a small thermostatically controlled electric motor. The smooth bore and freedom from rusting of copper tubes make them ideal for use under these conditions, since the minimum of resistance is offered to the flow of the water. As a result, with copper smaller sizes of tube can often be used throughout the installation, thus effecting a considerable reduction in cost and a saving of space, and at the same time producing a much neater job. This saving of space is often an important matter, for example, in blocks of flats and offices where the mains are usually run in pipe ducts or chases.

PANEL HEATING

As an alternative to the hitherto more conventional radiator system of heating, it has long been realised that the warming of comparatively large areas of floor, wall or ceiling surfaces provides a very comfortable and efficient form of radiant heating, with the result that the system known as "panel heating" has become popular.

In such a system, warm water is circulated through panels of closely spaced pipes, composed either of single lengths of pipe bent backwards and forwards or parallel lengths of pipe connected in grid form between headers, all of which are embedded just below the surface of ceilings, walls or floors.

Panel heating is now used extensively, particularly in America, and it is interesting, therefore, to note that the idea was first used in modern building in Great Britain, where there are to-day many installations in service, notable amongst them being those in the Bank of England building in London and the Bodleian Library in Oxford. (See Plates XVII and XVIII, facing p. 97.)

It must not be thought that panel heating can be applied only to large buildings.

Small houses are now often heated in this way, the cost, in suitable circumstances, being little if any greater than that of the more conventional type of heating installation.

Unlike the usual radiator type of installation, in which most of the heat is transmitted to the surrounding air by convection, with panel heating the heat is transmitted mainly by radiation from the surface of the ceiling, wall or floor in which the pipes are embedded. A pleasant sense of warmth is thereby created which is largely independent of the temperature and circulation of the air within the space to be heated.

Choice of Position for Panels

The best designed systems of panel heating are those which use large areas of surface at relatively low temperatures to give the necessary degree of heating. The mass of material surrounding the panel coils necessarily gives rise to a certain amount of lag between the time of heat input and that at which the effects are felt. A relatively thin covering of the panels is therefore desirable and, in consequence, it is usually preferable to locate the panels in ceilings or walls rather than in floors. From the point of view of comfort, also, ceiling panels are often preferred, as floor panels may tend to give rise to foot discomfort unless the temperature is kept relatively low.

Forced Circulation

With the long lengths of pipe required in panel heating, it is evident that the very smooth internal surfaces of copper tubes, and their freedom from rust, are important advantages, since they give rise to a comparatively low frictional resistance to the flow of water and greatly facilitate its circulation. Moreover, a smaller size of pipe can be used with copper than with iron or steel to perform the same duty.

With correct design, particularly in relation to pipe sizing and layout, an adequate natural circulation of water can be maintained in many of the smaller types of panel heating installation, but in other cases a forced circulation by pump is required for the most efficient results. A rough method of determining the size of pump required will be found on p. 100 (Table XX).

Advantages of Copper Tube

In addition to the above-mentioned important attribute of copper tubes for panel heating, they have other special advantages. They are light, easy to handle and fix and are obtainable in lengths up to 120 ft. in coil. They are extremely easy to bend and thus can be manipulated to any shape required in the panels with the use of a minimum number of joints. Where joints are required, they can be made easily and economically by any of the methods already described in previous chapters (see pp. 21–41).

The relatively small volume of metal in the walls of light gauge copper tubes means that their heat content is reduced to a minimum, so that they respond quickly to temperature changes, which helps to reduce the time lag in the response of the system as a whole. The high thermal conductivity of copper is also advantageous from the point of view of heat conduction.

Since panel heating pipes are buried in ceilings, walls or floors, it is essential that they shall not be corroded or damaged by the material with which they are surrounded. Copper has an exceptional resistance to corrosion and is not attacked by any normal type of cement, concrete or plaster and can safely be buried in these materials. It should not, of course, be brought into contact with acid plasters, acid cements or coke breeze, which will attack any type of metal, unless some form of protection is afforded.

Copper tube is adequately strong to withstand stresses set up by thermal expansion and contraction, while its coefficient of thermal expansion is sufficiently near to that of plaster and concrete to ensure that in operation stresses are reduced to a minimum.

Copper tube to British Standard 1386–1947 is entirely satisfactory for panel heating and by its use the overall cost of a copper installation is reduced to a highly economic and competitive level.

Size of Tube and Type of Coil

A range of sizes of copper tube is provided in B.S. 1386 from which a choice can be made. The size of tube selected will depend on the size and type of panel under consideration, but in general it is recommended that a tube not smaller than $\frac{1}{2}$ in. should be used, though in many cases a $\frac{3}{4}$ in. tube will give better results and will reduce the length of tube required. Headers and main connections will, of course, require the use of larger sizes of tube.

Panels may be made up either in the form of continuous return bent coils, laid out on site, as shown in Fig. 41 (A), which is the arrangement now generally preferred, or as grids between headers as shown in Fig. 41 (B). In the latter case, they are generally made up off site and may be used singly or in multiples according to the area to be heated.

Importance of Correct Layout

In any but the simplest type of installation, careful consideration must be given to designing the layout of pipes so that there is a correct distribution of water through the various coils. Any possibility of short-circuiting must be avoided and pipe sizes must be selected so that a correct balance is obtained as nearly as possible. Flow and return legs to individual coils should be kept as nearly the same length as possible, and balancing valves should be fitted where necessary so that flow can be accurately controlled. The direction of flow should preferably be away from outside walls inwards. Venting and drainage must also be provided for.

These considerations apply equally to gravity and forced circulation systems.

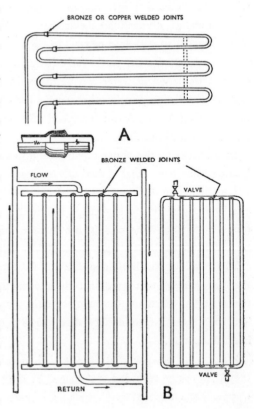

Fig. 41.   Heating panels of light gauge copper tubes.

PLATE XVI.   *Forming copper tube end for manipulative compression fittings.   (See p. 23.)*

To face page 96.

PLATES XVII *and* XVIII. *Panel heating coils fabricated from soft copper tube.*
(*See p.* 94.)

Where floor panels are used, it is common practice to run the tube on to the rough slab or floor filling in such a way that it is from $1\frac{1}{2}$ in. to 3 in. below the finished surface.

In ceilings, the tube should be secured against laths or expanded metal and plastered over, so that there is not less than $\frac{1}{4}$ in. of plaster between the face of the tube and the finished surface of the ceiling and not less than the same thickness above the tube.

When fixed in ceilings below concrete or hollow block floors, the panels are laid out on the shuttering before the concrete and/or blocks are placed in position, so that they only require finally to be covered by the ceiling plaster.

In ceilings or walls of timber construction, or those made up of self-supporting units, panels may be secured to framework of light steel angles or bars, filled with a suitable pugging composition, covered with expanded metal and plastered over flush with the rest of the ceiling or wall.

When panels are fixed in ceilings immediately above which is a roof space or roof, or in ceilings below timber floors, it is advisable to insulate the panels with a layer of cork, glass or rock wool, or other suitable material placed on top of them. Similarly, the backs of panels placed in external walls should be insulated. A layer of waterproof insulation may also be laid with advantage below panels installed in solid ground floors.

The coefficient of linear expansion of copper is sufficiently near to that of concrete and plaster to ensure that within the normal range of temperatures required in panel heating, and with the lengths of straight pipe usually employed, undue stresses due to differential expansion and contraction will not occur either in the copper tube or in the material in which it is embedded. If, however, long straight lengths are necessary, it may be advisable to wrap the pipe with bitumen tape or other suitable material to allow some movement to take place. It is good practice to take this precaution on embedded straight runs over, say, 50 ft. in length and also to avoid very short straight lengths between relatively fixed points.

For a given temperature of panel, the heat dissipated per unit area is greatest from floor panels and least from ceiling panels, that from wall panels being intermediate between the two. For reasons of foot comfort, it is usual to operate floor panels at a lower temperature than either ceiling or wall panels, the temperature of which is limited only by the need to avoid causing discomfort to the occupants of the room and damage to the material in which the coils are embedded. The maximum surface temperature of ceiling and wall panels usually does not exceed about 100° F. and that of floor panels about 85° F.

It is not possible within the scope of this book to give full and precise details for the design of panel heating installations and those requiring such details are advised to consult a good manual on the subject.* As a very rough guide, however, to the design of a small installation, the following notes may be helpful. They do not pretend to deal with the matter at all completely, but since in any case a number of assumptions has

Fixing of Panels

Thermal Insulation

Thermal Stresses

Temperature of Panels and Heat Required

Design Details

* *e.g.* " Radiant Heating " by T. Napier Adlam.

G

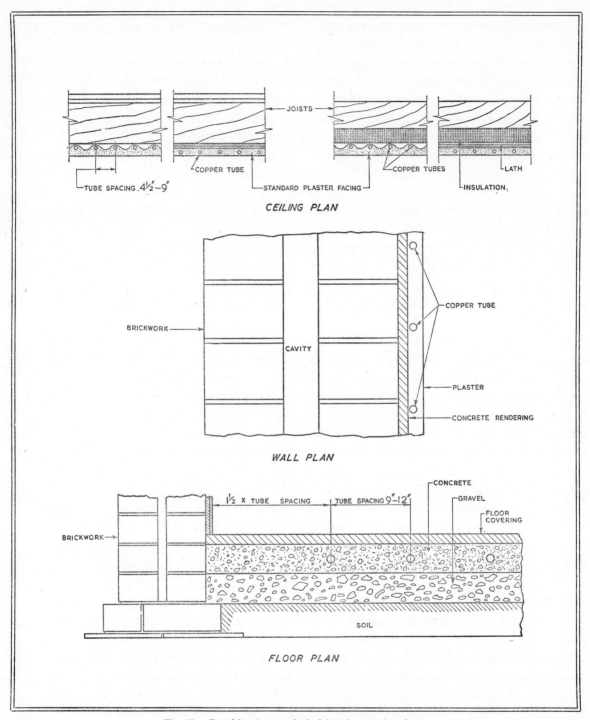

CEILING PLAN

JOISTS

TUBE SPACING 4½"−9"

COPPER TUBE

STANDARD PLASTER FACING

COPPER TUBES

LATH

INSULATION

WALL PLAN

BRICKWORK

CAVITY

COPPER TUBE

PLASTER

CONCRETE RENDERING

FLOOR PLAN

CONCRETE

GRAVEL

FLOOR COVERING

1½ × TUBE SPACING

TUBE SPACING 9"−12"

BRICKWORK

SOIL

Fig. 42. Panel heating: method of forming panel surfaces.

to be made and there are many factors which are not susceptible to exact determination, they will probably be sufficient as a rough guide in the design of the simple type of installation to which they are intended to apply.

In order to make this simplification possible, the choice of pipe sizes and spacings has been restricted and the following assumptions have been made:—

1. That the structures of ceilings, walls and floors resemble those shown in Fig. 42 and that, in floor panels, the centre-line of the tubes is about 3 in. from the floor surface.
2. That the desired room air temperature is to be 65° F.
3. That the average water temperature in ceiling panels is 140° F., in wall panels 135° F., and in floor panels 110° F.
4. That the maximum temperature of the floor surface does not exceed 85° F.
5. That the maximum total hydraulic pressure drop in the installation is 6 ft.
6. That the pipes are in conformity with British Standard 1386 and that their nominal sizes are $\frac{1}{2}$ in. for ceiling and wall panels and $\frac{1}{2}$ in. or $\frac{3}{4}$ in. for floor panels.

The design procedure is as follows:—

(*a*) Calculate the Heat Loss in B.T.U. per hour of the room to be heated. This may be done by any of the recognised methods used by heating and ventilating engineers.

(*b*) Select the type of panel to be used and calculate the area required by dividing the heat loss by the rated output of the panel as given in the following table.

TABLE XIX

Location of Panel	Panel Tubes		Rated Output of Panel, B.T.U./hr./sq. ft.
	Nominal Size, in.	Spacing C. to C., in.	
Ceiling	$\frac{1}{2}$	6	58
	$\frac{1}{2}$	9	40
Wall	$\frac{1}{2}$	6	63
	$\frac{1}{2}$	9	45
Floor..	$\frac{1}{2}$	9	50
	$\frac{3}{4}$	9	53

In some cases, it may be necessary to use more than one type of panel if it is not possible or convenient to obtain the necessary area all in one panel (e.g. a wall panel may be needed to augment a ceiling panel).

(*c*) The total length of tube required is next determined by multiplying the panel area by a factor of 2 for 6 in. spacing and of 1·3 for 9 in. spacing.

(*d*) So that the total hydraulic pressure drop shall not exceed the assumed maximum, panel circuits should be arranged in parallel so that each such circuit contains not more than 120 ft. of $\frac{1}{2}$ in. tube or 200 ft. of $\frac{3}{4}$ in. tube.

(*e*) The size of the tube required to feed various numbers of panel circuits can be obtained from Table XX below, which also indicates the minimum capacity of circulating pump required. (The length of main from the boiler to the farthest coil should not exceed 100 ft.)

TABLE XX

Nominal Size of Tube, in.	Number of Panel Circuits		Miminum Pump Capacity at 6 ft. Head, Galls. per Min.
	$\frac{1}{2}$-in. Tube	$\frac{3}{4}$-in. Tube	
$\frac{3}{4}$	1	—	—
1	3	1	4
$1\frac{1}{4}$	6	3	8
$1\frac{1}{2}$	9	4	12
2	20	10	25

COPPER TUBES FOR STEAM SERVICES

In view of the growth of interest in the use of copper for the conveyance of steam, the following brief section is included.

Copper is more flexible than steel, which is an advantage, but it is apparent that for large diameters and high pressures and temperatures a limit is imposed, either by the increased cost or lack of the necessary mechanical strength.

Lloyd's Rules

For many years Lloyd's Rules have been typical of general practice and have proved entirely satisfactory so far as copper pipes are concerned. The Rules limit the diameter of pipes to 5 in. for working pressures over 180 lb. per square inch, and state that copper can be used for temperatures up to 425° F. Permissible working pressures are:

If t = thickness of metal in hundredths of an inch;
d = diameter of pipe in inches;

For brazed copper, working pressure = $\dfrac{45\,(t-3)}{d}$ lb. per square inch.

For solid drawn copper, working pressure = $\dfrac{60\,(t-3)}{d}$ lb. per square inch.

B.S. 1306

More recently British Standard 1306, Part 1, 1946, covering non-ferrous pipes and pipe installations for and in connection with land boilers, was issued. This applies to copper pipes up to 5 in, bore for steam pressures up to 250 lb. per square inch at temperatures up to 405° F. and to feed-water pipes up to 8 in. bore for water pressures up to 300 lb. per square inch and 300° F. Suitable sizes and thicknesses of copper pipes with both plain and screwed ends are specified in B.S. 1306, Part 2, 1947.

Large diameter copper pipes are used for such purposes as exhaust steam mains and are often constructed of riveted or welded sheets. Brazed seams between sheets in such pipes are unreliable and should not be used. Smaller diameter copper pipes are much used for condenser mains in steam heating and other installations, and for these, as well as for lower duty steam pipes in which the temperature does not exceed 302° F., copper tubes to B.S. 659 or B.S. 61 may be used.

The normal method of jointing copper steam pipes is by means of flanges, which may be either of the fixed or loose type. Fixed flanges of brass or mild steel are either brazed to a plain tube in the manner described on p. 36, or for tubes up to 4 in. in diameter may be screwed and brazed, in which case thick-walled tubes must be used. Loose flanges are used in conjunction with brass collars brazed to plain tube ends and may be of brass, gunmetal, or mild steel. B.S. 1306, Part 1, 1946 deals with flanged joints and other design details.

Joints for Steam Pipes

For saturated steam pressures up to 100 lb. per square inch standard screwed fittings are used for the smaller tubes (under 4 in.). Compression fittings are also used for pressures up to 150 lb. per square inch, more particularly in the smaller diameters (up to $1\frac{1}{4}$ in.), and capillary fittings with various soft solders are employed for the pressures given on p. 29, while the use of a silver solder or brazing spelter should make them satisfactory for the higher temperatures when the nature of the work allows brazing to be easily carried out.

Expansion joints suitable for steam services are described on p. 60.

CHAPTER XI

SANITATION

The use of light gauge copper tubes for sanitary services during the past fifteen years has proved all the claims made for the metal. Copper, being a "kind" metal, can be worked to follow the contours of a building without deformation of the bore. The jointing can be done by welding or hard-soldering, either by forming the necessary sockets and branches from the tube itself or by the use of weldable bronze or electro-formed copper fittings for the larger sizes. On waste and vent pipes, compression or capillary soldered

Advantages of Copper Tubes

fittings are very often used and a number of manufacturers have special waste fittings available in sizes up to $2\frac{1}{2}$ in. (see Plate XXV*b*, facing p. 112). The advantages of copper tubes for sanitary installations can be briefly stated as being light in weight, easy to handle, work, bend, joint and fix. They are strong yet ductile and are highly resistant to corrosion without the need for internal or external protection; because of smooth surfaces and no rusting, copper pipes are self-cleansing and ensure free flow. In addition, the small overall diameter of copper pipes, particularly at joints, greatly facilitates installation in confined spaces. Permanently gas-tight joints can be assured and the maximum use of off-site preparation is possible. Copper pipes do not creep and are unharmed by normal thermal stresses. All these factors combine to give economy in installation and maintenance at a cost lower than would be the case with other comparable materials.

These qualities of copper have been found of particular advantage in "one pipe" sanitary installations in large blocks of flats and hotels. In these installations the sanitation pipes are generally grouped in internal ducts, and in the case of a large block of flats in the centre of London, it was estimated that by using bronze-welded light gauge copper tubes the saving in space due to the smaller ducts required was alone sufficiently great to make the use of copper desirable.

Cleansing Agents

When liquid cleansers and bleaching agents are used in accordance with the manufacturer's instructions they should not have any deleterious effect on metals. If, however, they are used in excessive amounts, or are allowed to remain in contact with metals, corrosion troubles may occur.

Regulations Governing Use of Copper Sanitation Pipes

The use of copper pipes for soil, waste and ventilating pipes is now allowed by almost every local authority. The gauges for the various diameters of tube up to 6 in. are laid down by B.S. 659–1955—Sanitation Tubes and are given in Table V, p. 19.

The L.C.C. regulations stipulate that soil and vent pipes shall be not less than 3 in. internal diameter. There has been some controversy about using main pipes of this

102

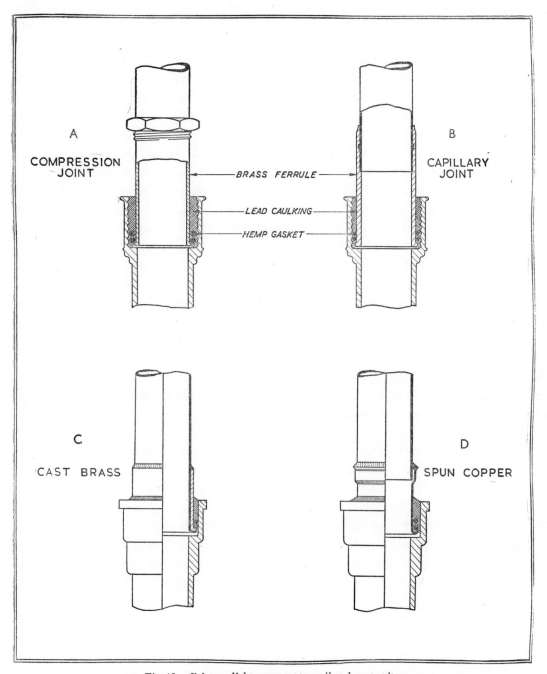

A

COMPRESSION
JOINT

B

CAPILLARY
JOINT

BRASS FERRULE

LEAD CAULKING

HEMP GASKET

C

CAST BRASS

D

SPUN COPPER

Fig. 43. Joints to light gauge copper soil and waste pipes.

diameter, but tests have shown that for ordinary domestic dwellings it is large enough to carry all normal discharges. In America 3 in. is almost universally used for private houses.

Jointing of Copper Pipes to Drains and Appliances

The methods of jointing mentioned earlier are all approved by the various authorities concerned. For details of joints used where a copper soil pipe enters a drain or terminates at a W.C. pedestal, the reader is referred to the illustrations in Fig. 43, p. 103. In *A*, the pipe is connected to a cast iron pipe by means of a caulking socket with a ferrule having a compression joint at the copper end. *B* varies only in that the copper end has a capillary soldered joint. Both fittings are made of cast gunmetal. The caulking is done with spun yarn grummets and molten lead or lead wool well drifted in. At *C* a cast brass socket, welded or hard-soldered to the copper, is used. *D* shows a spun copper socket joined to the copper tube by welding or hard-soldering; in each case the joint with the cast iron is made as in *A* and *B*. In the case of stoneware drains the same fittings are used but the lead caulking is replaced with Portland cement. In Fig. 44, p. 105, the connection to a W.C. outgo is shown. *A* illustrates a cast brass thimble welded to the copper; *B* is a short spun copper thimble; *C* illustrates a length of copper tube one end of which is formed by machine as a thimble; the other is left plain to be connected direct to the soil pipe itself. This item is obtainable in varying lengths up to and including 3 ft. The actual connection to the pedestal is by spun yarn grummets and either Portland cement or red-lead putty.

Jointing of Copper to Pipes of Other Metals

Where a copper pipe is connected to lead, a brass connector or union must be used. One end of the connector has a plain tail to join to the lead with a wiped solder joint, the other end being connected to the copper by one of the methods mentioned earlier.

Where brass ferrules, thimbles or connectors are used to make a joint between copper and pipes of other materials, they should be of good quality and in accordance with B.S. 1182–1944. Alternatively cast gunmetal, spun or preformed copper thimbles and ferrules can, of course, be used.

Fittings for Jointing Copper Pipes

While capillary and compression fittings and brazing, as already described, are suitable means of jointing copper waste pipes from baths, lavatory basins and sinks, etc., these methods are for economic and practical reasons not at present normally used for sizes larger than $2\frac{1}{2}$ in. In America, however, capillary fittings are used extensively for soil stacks up to 8 in.

In this country electroformed copper soil pipe sockets and branches are being used with soft or silver solder as a jointing medium. It must be pointed out that this is not a capillary fitting. These fittings are relatively cheap, but their use is not recommended on multi-storey installations. Where a number of branches enter the main stack in close proximity, the whole unit can be readily made by the electrodeposition process, thereby further reducing the cost of the installation. Plate XIX shows an example of a complicated branch piece so formed.

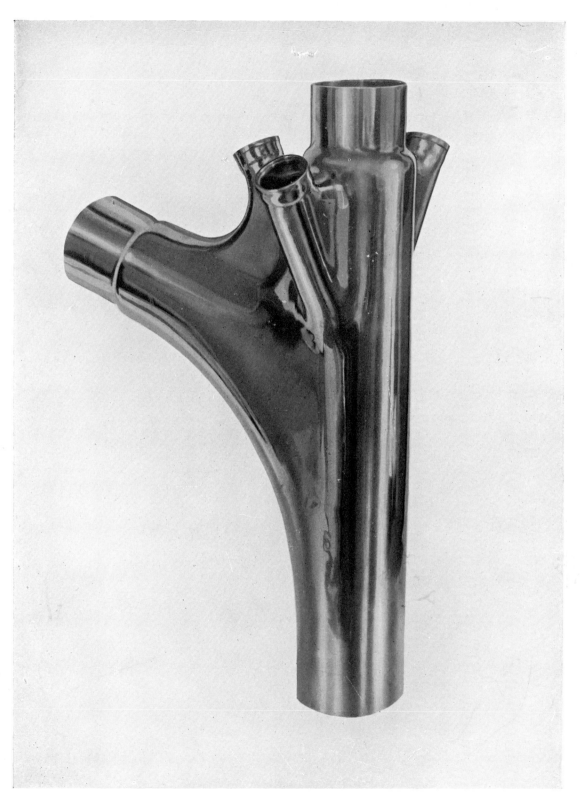

PLATE XIX.   *Electroformed copper soil pipe junction.*   (*See p.* 104.)

To face page 104.

PLATE XX.   *Softening the metal of a light gauge copper soil pipe preparatory to cutting a slit between the two drilled holes before working out a branch socket.   (See p. 106.)*

PLATE XXI.   *Working or "tafting" out the soil pipe to form a socket for a bronze welded branch joint.   (See p. 106, and Plates XXII and XXIII, opposite.)*

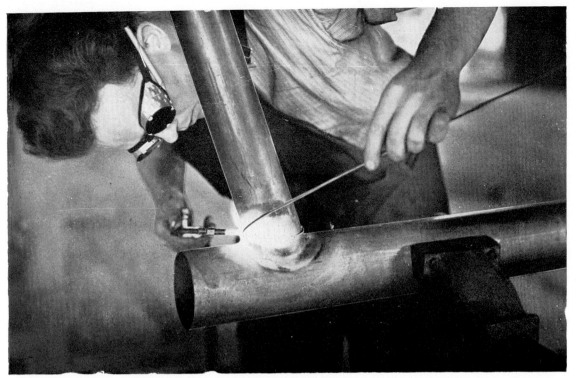

PLATE XXII.   *Bronze welding a branch to the socket worked out from a light gauge copper soil pipe.   (See p. 107.)*

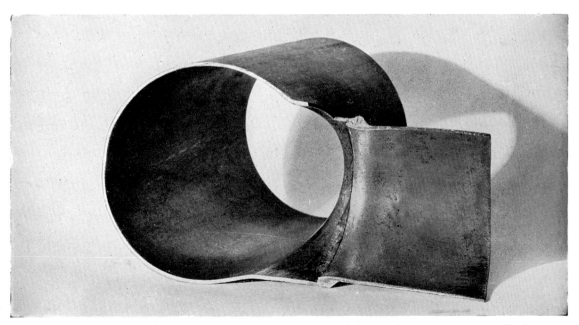

PLATE XXIII.   *The section of a bronze welded branch joint to a light gauge copper soil pipe. (See p. 107.)*

PLATE XXIV. *Prefabricated copper soil pipe installation.* (See p. 106.)

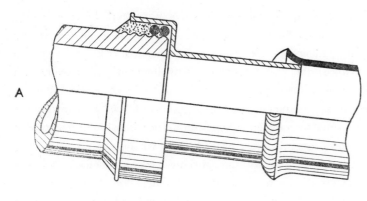

CAST BRASS — BRONZE WELDED

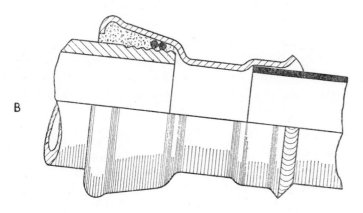

SPUN COPPER — HARD SOLDERED

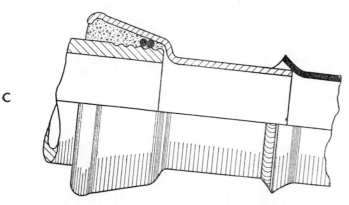

SPUN COPPER — AUTOGENOUSLY WELDED

Fig. 44.   Connections to W.C. outgo.

Special Weldable Fittings

It is of interest that in one bronze welded one-pipe sanitary installation in a large block of flats, the short branch picking up two back-to-back W.C.s was cast in gunmetal in one piece, including the connecting thimbles to the W.C.s and the short sockets for the anti-siphonage pipes. The cast bronze branch was then bronze welded to a socket tafted out from the main soil pipe and the copper anti-siphonage pipes were bronze welded to the sockets on the casting. Such castings are not standard and would not be economical except in large numbers for repeated sets of W.C.s, such as those in the installation mentioned.

Prefabrication and Off-Site Preparation

Reference has been made earlier to off-site preparation of copper soil and waste installations. Many of the largest plumbing contractors are now using copper pipes for such work because of the qualities mentioned at the beginning of this chapter and they have proved beyond all doubt that where a number of repeating sets are required the prefabrication method considerably reduces the cost by saving many hours of site labour. It is quite common to find that a one-pipe system unit can be bench-fabricated in six hours and be site-fitted in three hours or less; when the total labour time involved is compared with the time taken to complete a cast iron or cast iron-lead installation, it will be readily apparent how great a saving is made. It is not without interest that corresponding savings have been effected with prefabricated copper domestic hot and cold plumbing units. It must not be imagined that the savings are in any way made by sacrificing quality of workmanship; the bench fabrication is almost wholly carried out by skilled workers and craftsmen under ideal conditions and in circumstances which make thorough testing and inspection possible in a way seldom found on site. Plate XXIV (facing p. 105) illustrates a prefabricated copper soil installation.

When branch fittings are not employed, the opening and working of the holes in the main pipes to receive branches is not at all difficult in copper pipes. The main is first drilled with two small holes about 1 in. inside the proposed outline of the finished hole (see Plate XX, facing p. 104). The pipe is softened locally by means of a welding flame, and a slit is then cut between the two holes in the softened copper. This may be done by

driving a knife from hole to hole with a hammer. Alternatively, this slit can be made with the point of a ferret hacksaw. A tool can be improvised by riveting a piece of broken hacksaw blade between two pieces of wood for a handle. After levering the edges up, the sharp end of a "bent-bolt" is inserted and is then struck in an upward direction. When the hole is large enough to receive it, a piece of iron barrel with a socket tightly screwed on is inserted. The flame is applied until the edge of the copper, intended to form the socket, is red hot. The hole is opened with the copper red hot to avoid tearing of the edge, and care must be taken not to strike any point which is not at red heat (see Plate XXI, facing p. 104). The socket and

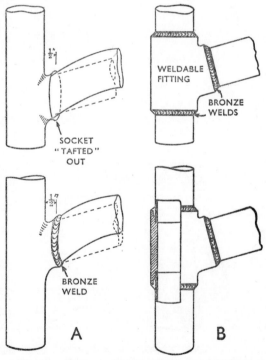

Fig. 45. Bronze welded branch joints to soil pipes.

branch should be made a true and tight fit to prevent drops from the bronze filler rod escaping inside, and care should be taken that the branch does not project inside the main. The edge of the socket, formed as described, should be belled out to form a small cup for the deposited reinforcing bronze filler metal. For joints to a vertical main this cup should not project more than about $\frac{1}{8}$ inch. Fig. 45, A, shows the joint diagrammatically. Plate XXII (facing p. 104) shows the operator bronze-welding the joint with the oxy-acetylene flame. Plate XXIII (facing p. 104) shows a cut section of such a branch joint. It can be seen that the joint is the strongest part of the pipe.

Branch joints made by cutting a hole in the main pipe of the size and shape of the inside of the branch, shaping and butting the branch over the hole, and bronze welding round the junction, are not suitable for waste and soil pipes, since there is a risk of the inside of the joint being obstructed by the weld and a properly swept junction may not be formed. Such joints may, however, be used for vent pipes where there is no question of a flow of liquids. A method of preparing this type of joint has already been mentioned under "Jointing Methods" (see p. 40).

Although bronze welding, using a bronze or copper-phosphorus filler rod, is the most widely applied method of jointing the larger sizes of pipe in sanitation work, there is no reason why silver soldering should not be used, provided that the preparation of the work is done correctly. In the case of a branch joint, the large bell mouth to the socket must be opened up parallel and just wide enough to allow the branch pipe to enter as a tight push fit. Similarly a straight joint can be formed by expanding one tube end to form a parallel socket into which the other tube end is tightly and squarely fitted. Drifts and tube expanders are available for the preparing of such joints. If a proper tool is not available a parallel socket may be formed on the larger sizes of pipe by the use of a piece of iron barrel as large in diameter as will go inside the copper tube. The sharp arris of the iron should be filed to a smooth rounded edge to avoid injuring the copper tube. The barrel is then placed in a solid vice with about 1 in. projecting from the side of the jaws. The copper tube is slipped over the end and held level. The outside of the tube is then struck solidly on to the barrel forming the anvil, the tube being rotated slightly after each blow. The flat face of a hammer should be used, striking level and solidly all the time. This has the effect of forming a socket about $\frac{3}{4}$ in. deep. Care must be taken to keep the socket true and large enough to form a push-fit with the tube which has to enter it. The spigot end, and also the inside of the socket, should be cleaned and fluxed with paste flux, so that the brazing solder penetrates when it is in a fluid condition.

Silver Soldered and Brazed Joints

For the smaller sizes of pipes such as waste pipes to lavatory basins, brazing with a silver solder avoids the rather bulky appearance of the bronze welded cupped joint, and as copper-silver solders are approximately the same colour as copper, the brassy colour of bronze-welded joints can be avoided. Plate XXV (facing p. 112) indicates the high quality of finish and the neat, almost streamlined, appearance which can be obtained with copper tube in sanitation work. This work was carried out for a café in Sheffield by a firm who are experts in such work in copper. The complete range of waste, ventilation, and hot and cold water pipes are in copper, and are chromium-plated. A description of the work by the firm responsible is as follows: "The outlets of the traps are brazed into the vertical branch pipes, which are connected to the main horizontal waste by brazed joints and to the main $1\frac{3}{4}$ in. anti-siphonage pipe with union connections: the bosses which receive the union connections are brazed into the $1\frac{3}{4}$ in. anti-siphon pipe. The main 2 in. waste pipe, which is 12 ft. long, has therefore only one union connection in its length and forms a complete unit with the five vertical branches. Screwed unions are also provided in the vertical branches and in the traps. The arrangement of brazed-in unions provides easy facilities for cleaning purposes in case of stoppage." The brazed joints were made with a silver solder.

Copper and Brass Traps

For use with copper waste pipes it is desirable to employ copper or brass traps, which, on account of their smooth bore, reduce the accumulation of dirt and grease. Copper and brass S or P traps can be easily made up by the plumber from light gauge tube, by employing one of the bending methods which allow bends to be made to a small radius (see Chapter IV). The ends of the tube forming the trap can be suitably prepared for compression joints, and the bosses for cleaning eyes or vent pipes, if required, can be brazed in with a silver solder. S traps can be made by means of two bends with a compression joint connecting them, and if there are compression joints at the ends of the trap, it is easily taken down for purposes of cleaning, and therefore no cleaning eyes are necessary. Alternatively, cast brass or bronze traps are obtainable in various types, including anti-siphonage traps. Fig. 46 shows some types of copper and brass traps.*

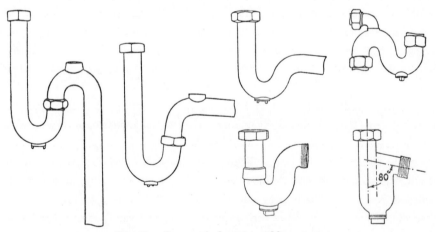

Fig. 46. *Some typical copper and brass traps.*

For purposes of reference it may be helpful to include here some typical examples of sanitary installations in light gauge copper.

* See also B.S. 1184, Non-ferrous (excluding lead) Traps and Wastes.

Fig. 47 is a diagram of a small house waste pipe installation executed in light gauge copper and discharging into a cast iron or stoneware drain. The main stack is 2 in., bath waste $1\frac{1}{2}$ in., sink $1\frac{1}{2}$ in., lavatory $1\frac{1}{4}$ in. The joints are bronze welded. The discharge of bath and lavatory wastes into a hopper or open rain-water head is not now generally approved, but there is little to be said against it in country districts where houses are far apart. The chief risk of smell and other objectionable features occurs when there are a number of such "heads" on the different floors of, for instance, a block of flats, especially if the drainage is within a light-well or a confined area between buildings. The sink is shown discharging into the stack. It can, of course, discharge separately to another back inlet of the gully-trap. The risk of the traps of the bath and lavatory basin losing their seals by siphonage with the pipe sizes and short wastes shown is rather remote, so that trap vents are not indicated. They are, however, always required by the L.C.C. by-laws. Where several branches discharge into one stack, and they are necessarily long owing to the position of the fittings, then the branches should always be trap vented if only to allow air to pass along the waste branches and oxidise the filth and keep it in the state known as "friable," i.e. so that it dries and shells off at succeeding flushes.

Fig. 48 shows a stack of three water-closets on different floors, branch ventilated and trap vented as in the best practice. A certain amount of trap vent could be omitted if, for

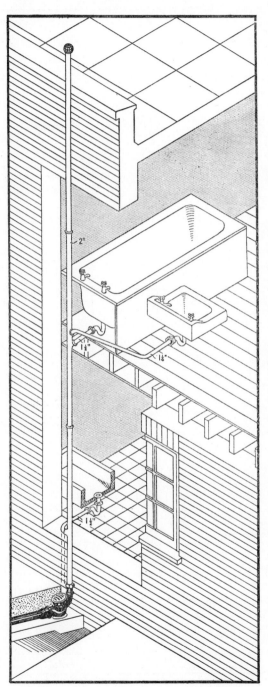

Fig. 47. *A typical light gauge copper waste pipe installation, with bronze welded joints.*

instance, the lower W.C. discharged separately to the drain, but there would be little saving, if any, in cost. Again, it is now ruled by many authorities to be unnecessary to trap vent the top W.C. on a stack if the branch is short. Hence the top vent shown could be omitted. The passover bends in the 2 in. branch vent could be avoided by carrying the vent-stack on the other side of the windows.

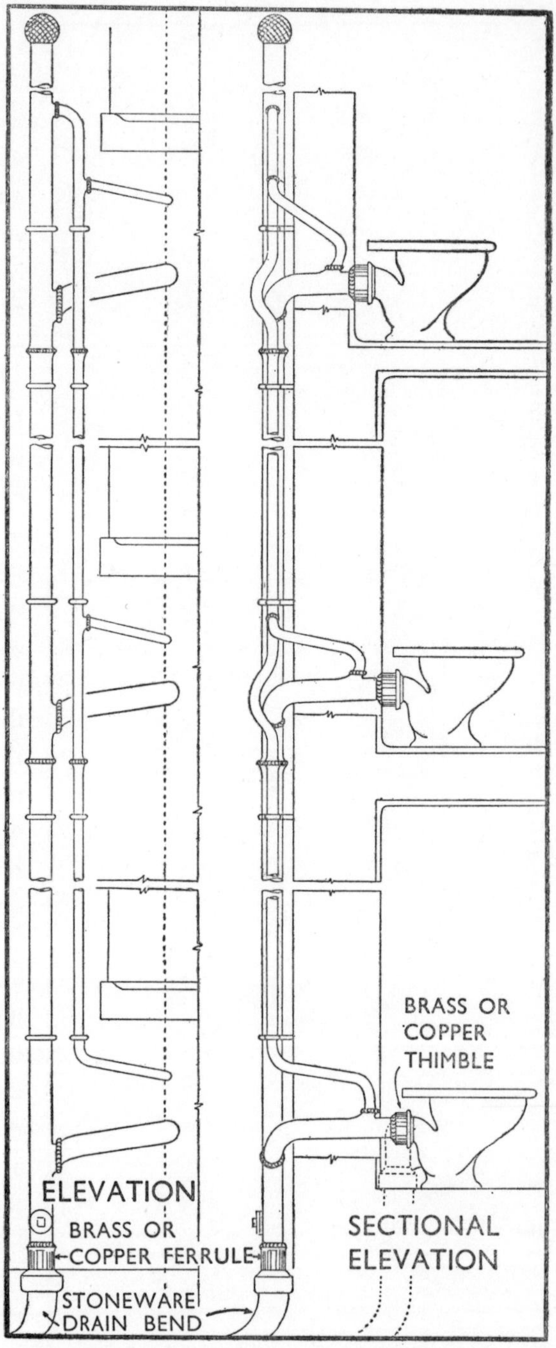

The arrangement shown is a typical external one. There is, however, an increasing tendency to fix sanitation pipes inside the building, and for this purpose light gauge copper tubes are especially suitable because of their general reliability, resistance to corrosion, and the saving in space effected by their small overall size compared with that of pipes of other metals, and by the fact that they require no painting and can therefore be fixed in chases or close to walls. It is, however, advisable to provide access to all inside pipes, whatever metal is employed.

One-Pipe System

The Ministry of Health and numerous other authorities have, by the wording of their specifications and by-laws, approved the discharge of waste water from ablutionary fittings into soil pipes. This approval, combined with the permissible grouping of soil and ventilating pipes in ducts within the building, has been welcomed by architects, as on high buildings with numerous

Fig. 48. *A typical light gauge copper external soil pipe installation, with bronze welded joints.*

fittings previous regulations created a network of costly and ugly pipes on the elevations.

Fig. 49 shows part of a one-pipe system on one floor of a building with internal plumbing. All the pipes, including heating, cold and hot supply, electric conduits, etc., are

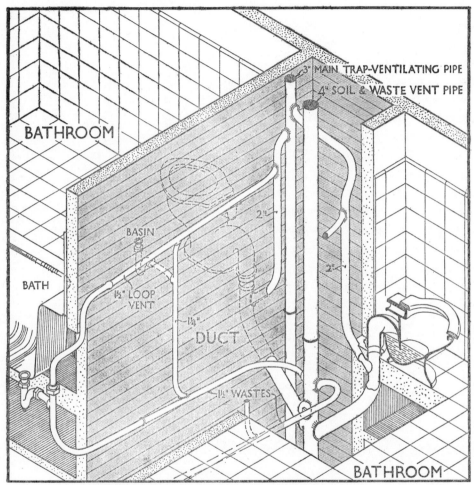

Fig. 49. Part of a one-pipe system in light gauge copper.

carried in the duct. Even the flushing cisterns and overflow pipes are carried in this space to produce a clean and tidy appearance in the bathrooms.* The bathrooms in the drawing are assumed to be back to back, with the duct between, which is common practice in modern hotel buildings, where a bathroom is often provided for each guest bedroom. The duct also forms the ventilating shaft for extracting and changing the air from the apartments by mechanical means. The sizes marked on the drawings are merely tentative, and the diameter of the main stack will depend upon the number of fittings

* Copper-lined W.C. flushing cisterns are covered by B.S. 1125–1945.

on the various floors discharging into it. With present building regulations governing heights of buildings in this country it is unlikely that a stack larger than 5 in. will be required for the domestic type of building. In the Mount Royal flats, London, with

eleven floors, the main stacks were 5 in. copper pipes and the branch vents 4 in. In Fig. 50 it will be noticed that two W.C. branches meet opposite each other on the main stack. For such circumstances it is recommended in the Institute of Plumbers' Minimum Specification that an oblique angle of 135° should be formed as shown in Fig. 50. These double junctions in light gauge copper can be easily formed by following the previous instructions as regards opening and welding. In some States of America an angle of

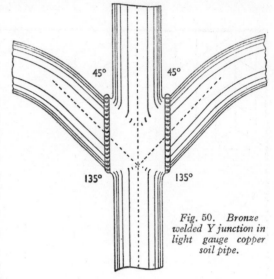

Fig. 50. *Bronze welded Y junction in light gauge copper soil pipe.*

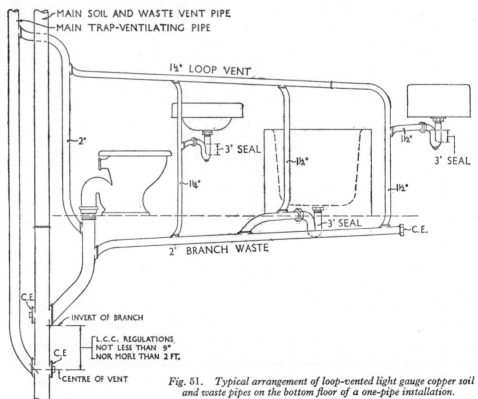

Fig. 51. *Typical arrangement of loop-vented light gauge copper soil and waste pipes on the bottom floor of a one-pipe installation.*

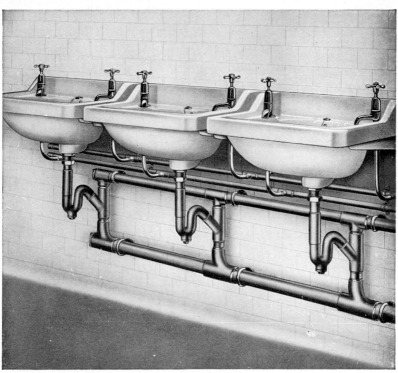

PLATES XXVa and XXVb.   A range of lavatory waste and anti-siphonage pipes in light gauge copper with joints in silver solder (Plate XXVa) and capillary soldered joints (Plate XXVb) respectively.   The service pipes are also of light gauge copper in both cases.

(See p. 107.)

To face page 112.

PLATE XXVI.   *Wall type copper radiators.*   (*See p.* 94.)

45° to the horizontal is required for all vertical branches entering soil pipes running in a horizontal direction.

Fig. 51 (p. 112) shows a typical layout of a group of fittings on a bottom floor discharging into one stack. The arrangement would be repeated on successive floors. The ventilation of the pipes is on what is known as the loop-venting principle, distinct from trap-crown venting, an example of which is shown in Plate XXV*b*. The drawing is made on one plane, for convenience, and the arrangement of the loop-vent may vary according to the placing of the sanitary fittings (cf. Fig. 49).

By reason of their lightness and rigidity, copper sanitation pipes require a minimum of fixing, and in general the smaller pipes used for wastes obtain sufficient fixing from the fittings to which they are attached, from branches, and from parts of the structure, though any particularly long unsupported lengths can be fixed by means of any of the types of pipe clips or brackets used in water service or heating work (see Fig. 26, p. 60). Similarly, vertical soil pipes obtain considerable support and rigidity from their branches which enter the building. They require, nevertheless, some form of fixing at approximately each floor of the building. This fixing may be made, in small installations, by means of a simple clip, such as those used for copper rain-water pipes, bolted to a lug which is built into the structure. For tall stacks it is usual to give greater support to the copper soil pipe by fixing it with holderbats placed immediately below the joints in the pipe, or below a small copper lug, bronze welded to the pipe, so that the stack obtains vertical support from each holderbat. Too much weight, however, should not be taken on the small copper lugs, otherwise a high local stress may be set up in the pipe wall, with a consequent risk of local buckling. It is claimed for weldable fittings that they form a good means of supporting the stack by placing a holderbat immediately below the fitting.

Fixing of Sanitation Pipes

The whole problem of the support of tall soil stacks is complicated by the expansion and contraction that may take place, due to the alternate discharge of hot and cold water in the one-pipe system. In America, where very tall stacks are usual, expansion joints of the bellows type have been employed to relieve any excess stress in the pipes, but for the maximum heights of buildings usually encountered in this country it is considered sufficient to provide a bend in the copper pipe at its foot, and in buildings in which the soil pipes are arranged in internal ducts, this can usually be conveniently arranged in the basement.

Much research on the discharge from sanitary fittings, and on pipe sizes, has been carried out by the Bureau of Standards of the United States Department of Commerce, and the results are summarised in their publication *Recommended Minimum Requirements for Plumbing*. The American system of determining the diameter of soil and waste pipes is based on the unit of the discharge from a lavatory basin having a $1\frac{1}{4}$ in. outlet. This unit represents a discharge of approximately 1 cu. ft. of water per minute, and is called a "fixture unit." Table XXI shows the minimum diameters of waste pipes for various

Rate of Discharge from Sanitary Fittings

H

TABLE XXI—*Discharges from Sanitary Fittings.*

Sanitary Fitting	Min. Diam. Waste	Fixture Units
	in.	
1 Lavatory basin	$1\frac{1}{4}$	1
1 House sink	$1\frac{1}{2}$	$1\frac{1}{2}$
1 Bath	$1\frac{1}{2}$	2
1 Hotel sink	2	3
1 Urinal (single basin)	$1\frac{1}{2}$	3
1 Shower	2	3
1 Slop sink	3	4
1 W.C.	3	6
A group consisting of 1 bath, 1 lavatory basin and 1 W.C. ..	—	8

TABLE XXII—*Pipe Sizes for Various Discharges.*

Maximum number of units that can be discharged into one stack having 45° Y inlets		
Diam. of Stack in.	In one Branch Interval	In whole Stack
$1\frac{1}{2}$	4	12
2	15	36
3	45	72
4	240	384
5	540	1020
6	1122	2070

fittings, and their discharge in terms of fixture units. It should be realised that the discharge of sanitary fittings is very intermittent, and taking this into consideration, by trial and observation, the discharges shown in Table XXII were determined.

A branch interval means a vertical length of stack not less than 8 ft. within which a branch or branches are connected, and the total units discharged from all branches connected to the stack within any 8 ft. length should not exceed the maximum shown in the table for one branch interval.

In soil wastes running in a horizontal direction with normal falls the number of units that can be connected to the branch is considerably less, and is shown in Table XXIII.

TABLE XXIII—*Discharges in Horizontal Branches.*

Pipe Diameter in.	Maximum Fixture Units		
	Fall $\frac{1}{8}$ in. per ft.	Fall $\frac{1}{4}$ in. per ft.	Fall $\frac{1}{2}$ in. per ft.
$1\frac{1}{4}$	1	1	1
$1\frac{1}{2}$	2	2	3
2	5	6	8
3*	15	18	21
4	84	96	114
5	162	216	264
6	300	450	600

* Not more than 2 W.C.s should be connected to a 3 in. branch.

The figures in these tables must necessarily be only an approximate guide for average conditions, since the pipe sizes depend upon the peak load, which (assuming that the number of sanitary fittings remains constant) will vary with different types of buildings. For example, the peak load in a factory will be greater than in a block of flats owing to the concentrated periods of use in the former.

CHAPTER XII

GAS FITTING

Until recent years copper was not used much for gas pipes except for the short lengths of exposed supply pipe to light fittings, geysers, gas fires, etc., where copper or brass tubes were sometimes used in order to obtain a neat appearance.* The usual materials employed for gas carcassing were iron, steel, lead and lead-compo; although some gas supply authorities were carrying out test installations with copper tubes with satisfactory results. Brass or copper pipes had, in the past, to have sufficient thickness of metal to take a screw thread, which meant that, as with water services, the use of copper tubes for the general run of gas supplies was ruled out on the score of high cost, in spite of obvious advantages; and whereas for water services the use of copper was in some districts essential, because of plumbo-solvent qualities of the water conveyed, this factor did not apply in gas installations. It is only since the development of the use of light gauge copper tubes by standardisation and suitable methods of jointing, which allow copper to compete economically with other materials, that it has been possible to take advantage of the excellent qualities of copper tubes for gas supply. The advantages of these qualities are now being realised by the gas industry, and although they are, in many cases, similar to the advantages for water services, it is thought desirable to summarise them briefly here.

Advantages of Copper Tube for Gas

Resistance to Corrosion. Copper tubes have a long life, and as they cannot rust there is no risk, as in iron pipes, of rust falling down a vertical pipe and choking the fitting at the foot, and no risk of fine rust choking nipples or meters. Maintenance costs are therefore reduced to a minimum.

Smooth Bore. As with water, the smooth bore of copper tubes gives a low frictional loss of pressure, and the absence of rust formation allows the maximum delivery of gas to be maintained indefinitely.

Small Sizes. As compared with pipes of other metals, copper tubes are smaller, and therefore lighter and neater, with the result that they are more easily buried in plaster and housed in the structure; notches in joists are smaller, and there is less hacking of brickwork, etc. The reduction in size is of particular advantage when installing or extending supply pipes in an existing building. Small sizes and lightness also make for easier handling and lower transport and storage costs.

Ductility. Light gauge tubes in the small sizes used for gas carcassing are easily

* For some important copper installations in this country and abroad, see C.D.A. publication No. 40, "Copper Underground: its Resistance to Soil Corrosion," pp. 31–40.

bent by one of the hand methods described in Chapter IV or by a small portable bending machine, with the result that the number of angle fittings is reduced and the use of bends in place of fittings again reduces loss of pressure.

Ease of Jointing. The use of compression fittings or capillary soldered fittings makes the jointing of light gauge copper tubes an easy matter, and reduces the number of tools required by the fitter, as compared with those used for iron tubing.

Speed in Fixing. The qualities of lightness and ease of jointing and bending allow light gauge copper gas pipes to be installed in a minimum length of time.

Safety. Copper pipes are not attacked by vermin and are highly resistant to damage by fire and electrical short circuits.

Tubing for gas installation work is covered by B.S. 1401–1947, "Copper and Brass Tubes for Gas Installation Work and Lighting Fittings." The sizes and thicknesses of tubes therein specified are identical with those in B.S. 659–1955, so that the same tubes may be used for both water and gas. **Light Gauge Tube for Gas**

The light gauge tubes may be of the usual half-hard temper, but for gas supply there may sometimes be advantages in using annealed tube, which can be obtained in coils of long length, and in this form is easily threaded through ducts, floor spaces, stud partitions, etc. In America, where companies have adopted light gauge copper tubing and capillary fittings for gas supplies, coils of soft annealed tube are largely used for underground work on the score of greater ductility and consequent reliability of the tube when subjected to settlements in ground or buildings. It is also the practice when replacing worn-out service connections and mains to thread the copper tube through the existing iron mains, so saving the expense of completely digging up the old mains.

In districts where the gas is dried before delivery to buildings, it may not be necessary to provide for possible condensation of moisture from the gas, but where the gas is not dried and the temperature may vary considerably, as, for instance, in pipes run out-of-doors, it may be advisable to lay the pipes to fall to given drainage points. In such instances it is advisable to employ tubes of half-hard temper.

Of the various jointing methods already described in Chapter III, those which are particularly applicable to gas services are compression fittings, capillary soldered fittings and bronze welding. All these methods provide a gas-tight joint, and the choice of one or another may depend upon the material and craftsmanship available. Where the supply pipes have to be buried in plaster or run under floors, capillary soldered fittings or bronze welding take up less space. For the details of all these methods of jointing, which are the same as for water service work, Chapter III should be consulted. **Jointing Copper Gas Pipes**

Copper can be safely buried in the majority of soils. The necessity for protecting copper tubes buried in certain acid soils has already been referred to in Chapter VII (see page 74) and applies equally to gas service pipes. Pipes may be protected by surrounding them with sand, chalk, broken limestone, slaked or well-burnt lime or other calcareous material. The methods commonly used for protecting iron and steel pipes may also be **Underground Gas Services** used for copper and consist of applying a coating of bitumen or pitch, either by itself, or reinforced with canvas wound spirally round the tubes. This canvas and pitch binding may be wound on before delivery to the site and the ends, joints, etc., treated after the pipe is laid. An alternative means of protection which has been found satisfactory consists of laying the copper tube in a V-shaped trough formed of two thin wooden boards, and pouring liquid pitch into the angle to surround and cover the tube, so forming a permanent protection, even if the wooden trough decays. For further information on this subject, reference should be made to C.D.A. Publication No. 40, *Copper Underground: its Resistance to Soil Corrosion.*

Copper in contact with Acid Plasters and Coke Breeze

As already stated, lime plaster and renderings of Portland cement have no harmful effect upon copper, but it is known that certain plasters which have an acid content are corrosive to metal, and copper tubes should not be buried in such plasters without protection. Many of the hard plasters which are generally classed as Keen's cement are acidic, but hard neutral plasters of this nature are obtainable. Copper tubes to be buried in plaster which is under suspicion can, however, be easily protected by wrapping them with bitumen tape, painting them with bitumen or, if space permits, dubbing round them with lime plaster or Portland cement.

Coke breeze, when wet or damp, has a corrosive effect upon metals and copper tubes should be suitably protected when passing through breeze blocks, or when run in chases in breeze partitions, or when buried in breeze concrete.

CHAPTER XIII

COPPER ELECTRICAL CONDUIT

Although outside the main scope of this book, brief mention must be made of the use of copper tubing for conduit for carrying electrical wiring in buildings, especially as the growing popularity of copper conduit is due to reasons not dissimilar from those influencing the use of copper for water services and other installations. In particular, its freedom from rusting has served to extend the use of copper conduit in buildings where industrial atmospheres cause rapid corrosion of ferrous conduit. Copper conduit is also popular for a number of semi-outdoor applications, such as pavilions, bandstands, swimming pools and garden illumination, and for burying in concrete when water is liable to gain access to the conduit during installation. The excellent electrical conductivity of copper is an additional advantage, while its very high thermal conductivity tends to reduce condensation; the smooth bore of copper tubing permits the wires to be pulled through easily, not only when the conduit is new, but also after years in service, and the facility with which the copper tubes can be bent and fitted contributes to the economical cost of the whole installation.

A British Standard (No. 840–1939) for light gauge copper and copper alloy conduits, **Standard** with the necessary fittings, is available. Table XXIV gives the sizes and thicknesses **Sizes**

TABLE XXIV—*Copper Conduit Tube Dimensions.*

Conduit Designation Nominal Size	External Diameter	Internal Diameter		Weight per 100 ft.	Permissible Tolerances on Outside Diameter		Thickness		Permissible Tolerances on Thickness		Corresponding Steel Conduits Heavy Gauge, ext. dia.
					Plus	Minus			Plus	Minus	
in.	in.	in.	in.	lb.	in.	in.	S.W.G.	in.	in.	in.	in.
½	0·447	0·375	(⅜)	18	0	0·004	20	0·036	0·004	0·004	½
⅝	0·572	0·500	(½)	23	0	0·004	20	0·036	0·004	0·004	⅝
¾	0·705	0·625	(⅝)	32	0	0·004	19	0·040	0·004	0·004	¾
1	0·955	0·875	(⅞)	44	0	0·004	19	0·040	0·004	0·004	1
1¼	1·205	1·125	(1⅛)	56	0	0·004	19	0·040	0·004	0·004	1¼
1½	1·471	1·375	(1⅜)	83	0	0·004	18	0·048	0·004	0·004	1½
2	2·000	1·904	—	113	0	0·004	18	0·048	0·004	0·004	2
2½	2·500	2·372	—	188	0	0·006	16	0·064	0·004	0·004	2½

of tube and permissible tolerances, as commonly used, and likely to be standardised. Equivalent steel conduit sizes are also included in the table.

Conduit Boxes

The conduit boxes for use with copper tubing are usually cast in a suitable copper alloy such as gunmetal or silicon bronze, although boxes pressed from sheet brass or copper have also been employed. Standard malleable iron or pressed steel conduit boxes fitted with screwed copper or brass adaptors to receive light gauge copper tubes can be used quite satisfactorily in certain instances if required.

Jointing

Screwed joints with heavy gauge copper conduit have been used in some installations, as in the Bank of England and new House of Commons, but ordinarily, with thin-walled conduit jointing methods resemble those employed for light gauge copper water tubing. Compression joints have been used but capillary soldered and bronze welded joints are now more widely employed. Plate XXVII opposite shows a small panel of light gauge conduit jointed with soft solder capillary fittings; the inspection bends and conduit box are cast in copper alloy. Methods already described for bending, jointing and fitting copper tubing are clearly also applicable to copper electrical conduit. (See also Plate XXVIII.)

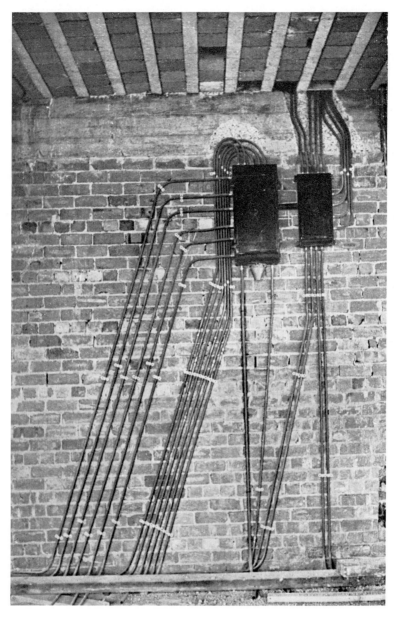

PLATE XXVII.   *Light gauge copper conduit entering distribution fuse box.*   (*See p.* 120.)

To face page 120.

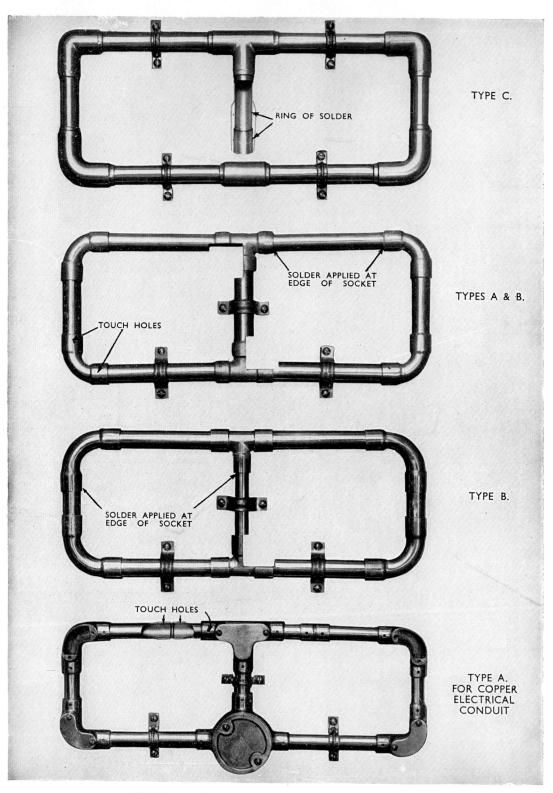

TYPE C.

RING OF SOLDER

TYPES A & B.

SOLDER APPLIED AT
EDGE OF SOCKET

TOUCH HOLES

TYPE B.

SOLDER APPLIED AT
EDGE OF SOCKET

TOUCH HOLES

TYPE A.
FOR COPPER
ELECTRICAL
CONDUIT

PLATE XXVIII.   *Typical capillary soldered joints for light gauge copper
tubes. (For reference to the Types* A, B *and* C, *see p.* 27.)

Title	B.S. No.	Reference in this book
		PAGE
Copper Tubes (Heavy Gauge) for General Purposes	61, Pt. 1–1947	16, 17
Screw Threads for Copper Pipes	61, Pt. 2–1946	18
Copper Alloy Three-piece Unions for Low and Medium Pressure B.S. Screwed Copper Tubes ..	66–1914	—
Copper-Alloy Pipe Fittings, Screwed, for Low and Medium Pressure B.S. Copper Tubes	99–1922	—
Malleable Cast Iron and Cast Copper Alloy Pipe Fittings (screwed B.S.F. taper thread) for Steam, Water, Gas and Oil	143–1938	—
Soft Solders	219–1949	30
Light Gauge Copper Tubes	659–1955	18, 19, 27
Copper Cylinders for Domestic Purposes (Grades 1, 2 and 3)	699–1951	89, 91
Copper Conduits for Electrical Wiring	840–1939	119
Electric Water Heaters	843–1939	89, 90
Calorifiers	853–1939	90
Capillary Fittings and Compression Fittings for use with Light Gauge Copper Tubes	864–1953	21, 27
Seamless Brass Tubes for General Purposes ..	885/6–1940	—
Water Taps, Bib, Pillar, Globe and Stop	1010–1953	—
Welded Joints in Copper Vessels	1077–1942	—
W.C. Flushing Cisterns	1125–1945	111
Non-ferrous Thimbles and Ferrules	1182–1955	104
Traps and Wastes, Non-ferrous (excluding lead) ..	1184–1951	108
Ball Valves (Portsmouth type)	1212–1953	—
Malleable Cast Iron and Cast Copper Alloy Pipe Fittings for Steam, Water and Gas (screwed B.S.P. taper male thread and parallel female thread)	1256–1945	—
Seamless Copper Tubes with Plain and Screwed Ends for Steam Service	1306, Pt. 2–1948	100
Copper Tubes to be Buried Underground ..	1386–1947	20, 74
Power-driven Circulators for Heating Plants ..	1394–1948	59
Copper and Brass Tubes for Gas Installation Work and Lighting Fittings	1401, 2 & 3–1947	117
Wrought Copper and Wrought Zinc Rainwater Goods	1431–1948	—
Fixing Accessories for Building Purposes	1494–1951	—
Copper Indirect Cylinders, Annular Type ..	1566–1949	89
Brazing Solder (Types 8, 9 and 10)	1845–1952	35

TABLE XXV—*Weights of Copper Tubes (pounds per foot).*

The weights given in this table are only for tubes having bores of the exact sizes shown in the first column. The table does not apply to tubes covered by British Standards 659–1944 *and* 1386–1947, *which have* nominal *bores (see Tables* IV to VI, *pp.* 18-20).

Thickness of Wall S.W.G. In.	20 0·036	19 0·040	18 0·048	17 0·056	16 0·064	15 0·072	14 0·080	13 0·092	12 0·104	11 0·116	10 0·128	9 0·144	8 0·160	7 0·176	6 0·192	5 0·212	4 0·232
Bore of Tube In.																	
$\frac{1}{8}$	0·07	0·08	0·10	0·12	0·15	0·17	0·20	—	—	—	—	—	—	—	—	—	—
$\frac{1}{4}$	0·12	0·14	0·17	0·21	0·24	0·28	0·32	0·38	—	—	—	—	—	—	—	—	—
$\frac{3}{8}$	0·18	0·20	0·25	0·29	0·34	0·39	0·44	0·52	—	—	—	—	—	—	—	—	—
$\frac{1}{2}$	0·23	0·26	0·32	0·38	0·44	0·50	0·56	0·66	0·76	—	—	—	—	—	—	—	—
$\frac{5}{8}$	0·29	0·32	0·39	0·46	0·53	0·61	0·68	0·80	0·92	1·04	—	—	—	—	—	—	—
$\frac{3}{4}$	0·34	0·38	0·46	0·55	0·63	0·72	0·80	0·94	1·07	1·21	—	—	—	—	—	—	—
$\frac{7}{8}$	0·40	0·44	0·54	0·63	0·73	0·82	0·92	1·08	1·23	1·39	—	—	—	—	—	—	—
1	0·45	0·50	0·61	0·71	0·82	0·93	1·04	1·21	1·39	1·57	1·75	—	—	—	—	—	—
$1\frac{1}{4}$	—	0·62	0·75	0·88	1·02	1·15	1·29	1·49	1·70	1·92	2·13	2·43	—	—	—	—	—
$1\frac{1}{2}$	—	0·74	0·90	1·05	1·21	1·37	1·53	1·77	2·02	2·27	2·52	2·86	—	—	—	—	—
$1\frac{3}{4}$	—	—	1·04	1·22	1·40	1·59	1·77	2·05	2·33	2·62	2·91	3·30	—	—	—	—	—
2	—	—	1·19	1·39	1·60	1·80	2·01	2·33	2·65	2·97	3·29	3·73	—	—	—	—	—
$2\frac{1}{2}$	—	—	—	1·73	1·98	2·24	2·50	2·88	3·28	3·67	4·07	4·61	5·15	5·70	—	—	—
3	—	—	—	—	2·37	2·68	2·98	3·44	3·90	4·37	4·84	5·48	6·12	6·76	7·40	—	—
$3\frac{1}{2}$	—	—	—	—	2·76	3·11	3·46	4·0	4·53	5·07	5·62	6·53	7·08	7·83	8·58	9·52	10·47
4	—	—	—	—	3·15	3·55	3·95	4·55	5·16	5·78	6·39	7·22	8·05	8·89	9·74	10·80	11·88

TABLE XXVI—*Theoretical Bursting Pressures for Copper Tubes to*

B.S. 659–1955
(*Half-Hard Temper*).

Diameter in.	Gauge	Bursting Pressure Lb./sq. inch
$\frac{1}{2}$	19	5900
$\frac{3}{4}$	19	4000
1	18	3600
$1\frac{1}{4}$	18	2880
$1\frac{1}{2}$	18	2400
2	17	2120
$2\frac{1}{2}$	17	1690
3	16	1610
$3\frac{1}{2}$	15	1560
4	14	1510
5	13	1465
6	12	1330

B.S. 1386–1947
(*Soft Temper*).

Diameter in.	Gauge	Bursting Pressure Lb./sq. inch
$\frac{1}{2}$	18	6100
$\frac{3}{4}$	17	4900
1	16	4100
$1\frac{1}{4}$	16	3300
$1\frac{1}{2}$	15	3100
2	14	2600
$2\frac{1}{2}$	13	2400
3	12	2200
$3\frac{1}{2}$	11	2100
4	10	2000

INDEX

124

LIST OF AVAILABLE C.D.A. PUBLICATIONS

GENERAL AND HISTORICAL

No. 3. *Copper Through the Ages.*

> An illustrated book for the general reader on the history of copper from ancient times to the present day (66 pp.).

„ 46. *Copper: its Ores, Mining and Extraction.*

> Describes with illustrations the world's chief copper ores, how they are mined, and how copper is extracted from them (54 pp.).

„ 52. *Introduction to Copper.*

> A brief account, copiously illustrated, of the history, mining and production of copper and its alloys, including the manufacture of wire, sheets, tubes, rods, etc., with notes on the products derived from these materials (52 pp.).

ARCHITECTURE AND PLUMBING

No. 25. *Copper Pipe-Line Services in Building.*

> A practical illustrated handbook for architects, builders and plumbers on copper tubes for water, sanitation, gas and heating services in building (128 pp.).

„ 40. *Copper Underground: its Resistance to Soil Corrosion.*

> Technical data on copper tubes, etc., buried in various types of soil (50 pp.).

„ 42. *Copper Flashings and Weatherings.*

> A practical illustrated handbook for architects, builders and plumbers, with detailed drawings of applications of copper sheet and strip in building (144 pp.).

„ 53. *'Economy' Copper Roofing.*

> This booklet deals with the laying of copper roofing strip in long lengths. It is copiously illustrated with working drawings on the same lines as publication No. 42, to which this is a companion volume (48 pp.).

AGRICULTURE AND HORTICULTURE

No. 41. *Copper Compounds in Agriculture and Industrial Microbiology.*

> An illustrated guide for farmers and agriculturalists on the use of copper compounds to combat plant diseases, etc. (118 pp.).

ELECTRICAL ENGINEERING

No. 22. *Copper for Busbars.*

> A comprehensive illustrated guide for use in the design of copper busbars for both indoor and outdoor installations (176 pp.).

„ 30. *Copper for Earthing.*

> An illustrated book on the protection of electrical installations by adequate earthing, using copper electrodes (56 pp.).

„ 37. *Mechanical Loading Tables for Overhead Line Conductors.*

> Tables for the preparation of sag and tension charts for overhead line installations, particularly those erected in Great Britain and countries of the British Commonwealth (10 pp.).

„ 38. *Copper Alloy Resistance Materials.*

> Describes the characteristics of resistance materials based on copper, their manufacture and their use in the construction of rheostats and resistances (44 pp.).

„ 45. *Copper Conductors for Overhead Lines.* (Reprinted from *I.E.E. Journal.*)

> An outline of the various factors to be considered in the design of overhead lines using copper, copper alloy and steel-cored copper conductors (55 pp.).

„ 51. *High Conductivity Copper Alloys.*

> Deals with four copper alloys—cadmium copper, chromium copper, silver copper, and tellurium copper—which are important primarily in the electrical industries (53 pp.).

No. 6. *Brasses.*
>A booklet for technologists on copper-zinc alloys, their properties and applications (54 pp.).

„ 12. *Copper Data.*
>A general guide providing information on the properties of copper and its working behaviour. The various grades and forms are described, and typical applications given (76 pp.).

„ 15. *Bearing Bronzes.*
>A booklet describing the range and properties of copper alloy bearings, including some notes on their installation (34 pp.).

„ 16. *Brass, Bronze and other Copper Alloy Wire and Wire Products.*
>A booklet devoted to production, treatment and applications of copper alloy wires (52 pp.).

„ 23. *Copper in Chemical Plant.*
>An illustrated book on copper and its alloys in the chemical industry, reviewing their properties, including corrosion resistance and describing typical plant (70 pp.).

„ 26. *Copper and Brass Pressings.*
>An illustrated book describing the principal processes employed in the manufacture of copper, brass, nickel silver and other copper alloy strip and sheet products, including blanking, deep drawing and spinning. Contains details of properties, composition and commercial tolerances of sheet, strip and foil (82 pp.).

„ 29. *Copper in Cast Steel and Iron.*
>A metallurgical account of the influence of copper on the manufacture and properties of iron and steel castings, with numerous diagrams and tables (132 pp.).

„ 31. *Aluminium Bronze.*
>A comprehensive account of the copper-aluminium alloys, their properties, production and applications; with numerous illustrations, diagrams and tables (168 pp.).

„ 34. *The Machining of Copper and its Alloys.*
>A practical handbook with illustrations, summarising modern practice and giving guidance on the selection of copper alloys for machined products (116 pp.).

„ 36. *Classification of Copper and Copper Alloys.*
>A booklet tabulating the compositions and mechanical properties of copper and copper alloys in wrought and cast forms, with references to the appropriate British Standards (28 pp.).

„ 39. *Copper and Copper Alloy Springs.*
>Describes the design and manufacture of springs, their characteristics and behaviour, as well as the criteria affecting the choice of suitable copper alloys (66 pp.).

„ 43. *Copper and its Alloys in Engineering and Technology.*
>An illustrated review of copper and its alloys showing how the particular advantages of each are utilised in various branches of engineering. Typical applications have also been tabulated (88 pp.).

„ 44. *Equilibrium Diagrams of Binary Copper Alloys.*
>A booklet containing forty-two equilibrium diagrams collected and edited for the convenience of metallurgists (49 pp.).

„ 47. *The Welding, Brazing and Soldering of Copper and its Alloys.*
>A detailed account of basic principles, the nature of the processes and materials employed; with copious illustrations and tables (190 pp.).

„ 48. *Copper in Instrumentation.*
>Deals in some detail with the use of copper and its alloys in pressure-responsive, electro-magnetic and temperature-responsive instruments (152 pp.).

„ 49. *Thermal Properties of Copper and Copper Pipes.*
>This booklet outlines the underlying principles of heat transfer and explains the saving due to the use of copper pipes (16 pp.).

„ 50. *The Strength of Copper Tubes and Cylinders.*
>Data showing the effects of service conditions and giving guidance on design (48 pp.).

Technical Survey of Progress in Copper and Copper Alloys.
>This is a critical commentary on current progress, with a useful bibliography, and is published in January and July each year.